Listen to the Spirit—
He Will Lead You
2015 Prayer Journal

A Reflection Journal Calendar
with the thoughts of Catherine Doherty

Trinity Photography

Listen to the Spirit—He Will Lead You 2015 Prayer Journal

Scripture is taken from the Good News Translation with Deuterocanonicals/ Apocrypha - Second Edition (c) 1992. American Bible Society, 1865 Broadway, New York, NY 10023, www.americanbible.org. Used with permission.

For information or **to order additional copies of this prayer journal**, contact:

Trinity Photography
3805 7th St. NE #109
Great Falls, MT 59404-1154
1-888-220-5941
catholicprayerdiary@gmail.com
http://www.catholicprayerdiary.com

Cover Photo: A cardinal in southern Arizona

ISBN: 978-0-9792942-7-3

Printed in Korea.

DEDICATION

*We dedicate this work
to Pope Francis and
to all the bishops of the world
in union with him.*

CATHERINE DOHERTY, SERVANT OF GOD

Russian-born Catherine Doherty emigrated to Canada shortly after the Bolshevik Revolution. Though able to support herself and her family in a comfortable fashion, she heard the Lord calling her to live and work with the poor. He revealed to her what she later called "The Little Mandate" (see below). She responded to His call, and from that, Friendship House and the Madonna House Apostolate were born.

Catherine's faith in God was the center of her life. The Catholic Church is currently studying her for canonization, for her practice of heroic virtue during her lifetime. In 2002, she was declared "Servant of God." (For more on Catherine's life, see the books listed on the Acknowledgements page).

The continuing process of considering Catherine for canonization now requires that three miracles, attributed to her intercession, be reported and verified. The following prayer has been devised by the Madonna House staff for those wishing to ask Catherine to intercede for their intentions:

All loving Father, through Your beloved Son, Jesus, we have been taught to ask for what we need. And through His spouse, our Mother the Church, we have been instructed to pray for one another, and to ask the intercession of Your servants, who have fallen asleep in Christ. Therefore, through the intercession of Your servant, Catherine Doherty, we ask (here mention your petition). We ask this for Your honor and glory, and in the name of Jesus Christ, Your Son Our Lord. Amen.

Imprimatur:
+J.R. Windle
Bishop of Pembroke
May 1, 1993

Favors received may be sent to:
Postulator, Madonna House
2888 Dafoe Rd., Combermere, Ontario
CANADA K0J 1L0

THE LITTLE MANDATE

Arise—go! Sell all you possess. Give it directly, personally to the poor. Take up My cross (their cross) and follow Me, going to the poor, being poor, being one with them, one with Me.

Little—be always little! Be simple, poor, childlike.

Preach the Gospel with your life—WITHOUT COMPROMISE! Listen to the Spirit. He will lead you.

Do little things exceedingly well for love of Me.

Love...love...love, never counting the cost.

Go into the marketplace and stay with Me. Pray, fast. Pray always, fast.

Be hidden. Be a light to your neighbor's feet. Go without fears into the depth of men's hearts. I shall be with you.

Pray always. I WILL BE YOUR REST.

MY HEART'S DESIRE
a prayer by Catherine Doherty

Grant, Thou, to my heart, a knowledge of the good, and to my mind, the gift of light to see. For Love by love alone is understood, and truth is only known when known in Thee. So may my intellect contemplate Thee until my heart falls prostrate before Thee...

O Jesus, my very own! Here is summed up my heart's desire: to love Thee ever more and more until I no longer live, and die from love! But let this love be not only of the mind and heart. Let it go forth and heal and help. Let it be found in the harvest of souls, brought back to Thy sacred fold!

O Jesus, prostrate before Thee, I beg only for one gift:

A blinding love of Thee,
An all-consuming love of Thee,
A supernatural love of Thee,
An all-enhancing love of Thee,
A gentle love of Thee,
A childlike love of Thee,
A love of Thee until death,
A love of Thee unafraid of martyrdom,
A love of all the poor in Thee,
A love of all the sick in Thee,
A love of all the strayed ones in Thee,
A love of all the sorrowful ones in Thee,
A love of all the lonely ones in Thee,
A love of all the little ones in Thee,
A love of all the scoffing ones in Thee,
A love of all sinners in Thee.

O Jesus, my prayer is:

Make me love Thee more and more,
and love everyone in Thee.

--

from Catherine's diary
August 20, 1934

NOTES ON CALENDAR CONTENTS
- Saints days, feasts and Church holy days follow the Roman Catholic liturgical calendars for the United States and Canada.
- **COLORS FOR MASS VESTMENTS** are given for each day.
- **HOLY DAYS OF OBLIGATION** are highlighted.
- Scripture readings listed for each day follow the Roman Catholic liturgical calendar of readings for Sunday Cycle B and Weekday Cycle 1, comprising the Mass readings for each day in 2015.
- Each Scripture quote is taken from one of the readings for that day.
- Civic holidays are listed for both the United States and Canada.

ACKNOWLEDGEMENTS

We gratefully express our appreciation to Madonna House Publications for permission to quote from the following sources:

<u>*by Catherine Doherty:*</u>
  Dear Parents: A Gift of Love for Families, 1997
  Donkey Bells: Advent and Christmas, 1994
  An Experience of God, 2002
  Beginning Again: Recovering your innocence and joy through Confession, 2004
  God in the Nitty-Gritty Life, 2002
  The Gospel without Compromise, 1995
  Grace in Every Season: Through the Year with Catherine Doherty, 1992
  In the Footprints of Loneliness: Meditations—when you hear an echo in your heart, 2003
  In the Furnace of Doubts: Meditations—when you've lost your answers, 2002
  Kiss of Christ: Reflections on the Sacrament of Penance and Reconciliation, 1998
  Light in the Darkness: A Christian Vision for Unstable Times, 2009
  Living the Gospel without Compromise, 2002
  Molchanie: The Silence of God, 1991
  On the Cross of Rejection: Meditations—when your heart is pierced, 2003
  The People of the Towel and the Water, 1991
  Poustinia: Encountering God in Silence, Solitude and Prayer, 2000
  Re-entry into Faith: "Courage—be not afraid!", 2012
  Season of Mercy: Lent and Easter, 1996
  Sobornost: Eastern Unity of Mind and Heart for Western Man, 1992
  The Stations of the Cross: In the Footsteps of the Passion, 2004
  Strannik: The Call to Pilgrimage for Western Man, 1991
  Urodivoi: Fools for God, 1993
  Welcome, Pilgrim, 1991

<u>*by others who quote Catherine extensively:*</u>
  Fathering: Building the New Civilization of Love, 2000
  Marriage: A Fountain of Grace, 2001
  Mothering: Becoming the Heart of the Home, 2000

To obtain copies of these books and other works of Catherine Doherty and Madonna House Publications, or to obtain information regarding progress in Catherine's canonization cause, contact:

Madonna House Publications
2888 Dafoe Rd., RR 2 • Combermere, Ontario, Canada K0J 1L0
1-888-703-7110
publications@madonnahouse.org
http://www.madonnahouse.org • http://www.catherinedoherty.org

FEELING REJECTED

Every human being deeply feels the rejection of his or her fellow man and, quite often, imagines that God also rejects him or her.

In as much as Christ was true man and true God, He felt rejection also. At least, that is my idea of the meaning of His cry on the cross. Being man as well as God, He accepted the sense of rejection experienced by every human being.

A psychiatrist named Jung made a tour of the world, analyzing nations and peoples. He concluded that all men feel rejected by God. He found that there was a deep rift at the bottom of men's souls, between themselves and that Someone greater than themselves... [But]...

God the Father says, "I have not rejected you. I have loved you from time immemorial. I have created you out of nothing, and you are Mine. I have made you what you are. I, God the Father, shaped you, God the Son died for you, God the Holy Spirit overshadowed you. You are not rejected. You are the friend of My Son, filled with peace and joy.

"If you have faith, rejection will lie at your feet and then disappear. I will never reject you. Therefore, be at peace. Your face reflects the face of My Son, as well as Mine. Rejection is a lie of the devil."

from: *On the Cross of Rejection: Meditations—*
when your heart is pierced, pp. 36-37, 40

ABOUT TRINITY PHOTOGRAPHY

Trinity Photography is a small brother/sister owned and operated business that publishes the Catholic prayer journal *Listen to the Spirit—He Will Lead You* yearly. As serious hobby-photographers, Dan Wedel and Sandy Wedel have been using their images in editions of *Listen to the Spirit...* since 1994. They are pleased to be able to use their camera skills to bring the wonder and the Word of God to others, and to help acquaint people with Servant of God Catherine Doherty, a clear example of holiness and wisdom for our modern times.

Dan Wedel is a commercial airline pilot and lives in a suburb of Chicago. Sandy Wedel is a retired religious education coordinator and teacher in northcentral Montana. Both are practicing Catholics faithful to the Magisterium of the Church. The Holy Spirit has given each of them a passion to help others learn about God's personal love for them, and how that is lived out in the Roman Catholic Church. This prayer journal is one of the means they hope will accomplish this goal.

2015

JANUARY

S	M	T	W	T	F	S
				1	2	3
4	5	6	7	8	9	10
11	12	13	14	15	16	17
18	19	20	21	22	23	24
25	26	27	28	29	30	31

FEBRUARY

S	M	T	W	T	F	S
1	2	3	4	5	6	7
8	9	10	11	12	13	14
15	16	17	18	19	20	21
22	23	24	25	26	27	28

MARCH

S	M	T	W	T	F	S
1	2	3	4	5	6	7
8	9	10	11	12	13	14
15	16	17	18	19	20	21
22	23	24	25	26	27	28
29	30	31				

APRIL

S	M	T	W	T	F	S
			1	2	3	4
5	6	7	8	9	10	11
12	13	14	15	16	17	18
19	20	21	22	23	24	25
26	27	28	29	30		

MAY

S	M	T	W	T	F	S
					1	2
3	4	5	6	7	8	9
10	11	12	13	14	15	16
17	18	19	20	21	22	23
24	25	26	27	28	29	30
31						

JUNE

S	M	T	W	T	F	S
	1	2	3	4	5	6
7	8	9	10	11	12	13
14	15	16	17	18	19	20
21	22	23	24	25	26	27
28	29	30				

JULY

S	M	T	W	T	F	S
			1	2	3	4
5	6	7	8	9	10	11
12	13	14	15	16	17	18
19	20	21	22	23	24	25
26	27	28	29	30	31	

AUGUST

S	M	T	W	T	F	S
						1
2	3	4	5	6	7	8
9	10	11	12	13	14	15
16	17	18	19	20	21	22
23	24	25	26	27	28	29
30	31					

SEPTEMBER

S	M	T	W	T	F	S
		1	2	3	4	5
6	7	8	9	10	11	12
13	14	15	16	17	18	19
20	21	22	23	24	25	26
27	28	29	30			

OCTOBER

S	M	T	W	T	F	S
				1	2	3
4	5	6	7	8	9	10
11	12	13	14	15	16	17
18	19	20	21	22	23	24
25	26	27	28	29	30	31

NOVEMBER

S	M	T	W	T	F	S
1	2	3	4	5	6	7
8	9	10	11	12	13	14
15	16	17	18	19	20	21
22	23	24	25	26	27	28
29	30					

DECEMBER

S	M	T	W	T	F	S
		1	2	3	4	5
6	7	8	9	10	11	12
13	14	15	16	17	18	19
20	21	22	23	24	25	26
27	28	29	30	31		

JANUARY 2015

Sunday	Monday	Tuesday	Wednesday	Thursday	Friday	Saturday
				1 Mary, Mother of God New Year's	2	3
4	5	6	7	8	9	10
11	12	13	14	15	16	17
18	19 Martin Luther King Day	20	21	22	23	24
25	26	27	28	29	30	31

FEBRUARY 2015

Sunday	Monday	Tuesday	Wednesday	Thursday	Friday	Saturday
1	2	3	4	5	6	7
8	9	10	11	12	13	14 Valentine's Day
15	16 Presidents' Day	17	18 Ash Wednesday	19	20	21
22	23	24	25	26	27	28

MARCH 2015

Sunday	Monday	Tuesday	Wednesday	Thursday	Friday	Saturday
1	2	3	4	5	6	7
8 *Daylight Savings Time Begins*	9	10	11	12	13	14
15	16	17 St. Patrick	18	19 St. Joseph	20	21
22	23	24	25	26	27	28
29	30	31				

APRIL 2015

Sunday	Monday	Tuesday	Wednesday	Thursday	Friday	Saturday
			1	2 Holy Thursday	3 Good Friday	4 Holy Saturday *Easter Vigil*
5 Easter	6	7	8	9	10	11
12	13	14	15	16	17	18
19	20	21	22	23	24	25
26	27	28	29	30		

MAY 2015

Sunday	Monday	Tuesday	Wednesday	Thursday	Friday	Saturday
					1	2
3	4	5	6	7	8	9
10 Mother's Day	11	12	13	14 **Ascension**	15	16
17	18 Victoria Day (Canada)	19	20	21	22	23
24 / 31	25 Memorial Day	26	27	28	29	30

JUNE 2015

Sunday	Monday	Tuesday	Wednesday	Thursday	Friday	Saturday
	1	2	3	4	5	6
7	8	9	10	11	12	13
14 Flag Day	15	16	17	18	19	20
21 Father's Day	22	23	24	25	26	27
28	29	30				

JULY 2015

Sunday	Monday	Tuesday	Wednesday	Thursday	Friday	Saturday
			1 Canada Day (Canada)	2	3	4 Independence Day
5	6	7	8	9	10	11
12	13	14	15	16	17	18
19	20	21	22	23	24	25
26	27	28	29	30	31	

AUGUST 2015

Sunday	Monday	Tuesday	Wednesday	Thursday	Friday	Saturday
						1
2	3 Civic Holiday (Canada)	4	5	6	7	8
9	10	11	12	13	14	15 **Assumption of the BVM**
16	17	18	19	20	21	22
23	24	25	26	27	28	29
30	31					

SEPTEMBER 2015

Sunday	Monday	Tuesday	Wednesday	Thursday	Friday	Saturday
		1	2	3	4	5
6	7 Labor Day	8	9	10	11	12
13	14	15	16	17	18	19
20	21	22	23	24	25	26
27	28	29	30			

OCTOBER 2015

Sunday	Monday	Tuesday	Wednesday	Thursday	Friday	Saturday
				1	2	3
4	5	6	7	8	9	10
11	12 Columbus Day (USA) Thanksgiving (Canada)	13	14	15	16	17
18	19	20	21	22	23	24
25	26	27	28	29	30	31

NOVEMBER 2015

Sunday	Monday	Tuesday	Wednesday	Thursday	Friday	Saturday
1 **All Saints** *Daylight Savings Time Ends*	2 All Souls Day	3	4	5	6	7
8	9	10	11 Veteran's Day (USA) Remembrance Day (Canada)	12	13	14
15	16	17	18	19	20	21
22	23	24	25	26 Thanksgiving	27	28
29	30					

DECEMBER 2015

Sunday	Monday	Tuesday	Wednesday	Thursday	Friday	Saturday
		1	2	3	4	5
6	7	8 **Immaculate Conception**	9	10	11	12
13	14	15	16	17	18	19
20	21	22	23	24	25 **Christmas**	26 Boxing Day (Canada)
27	28	29	30	31		

THE SKY OVER GRAND TETON NATIONAL PARK, WYOMING

"You will know that you were baptized for this: to bring *peace, harmony, love, faith and hope* to people, to those the Lord will allow you to meet through your life."

from *Sobornost: Eastern Unity of Heart and Mind for Western Man*

Thursday, January 1 \text{NEW YEAR'S DAY} - *HOLY DAY OF OBLIGATION*

THE SOLEMNITY OF MARY, THE HOLY MOTHER OF GOD *(White)*

"You are no longer a slave but a child. And since you are His child, God will give you all that He has for His children." (Gal 4:7)

Num 6:22-27
Ps 67:2-3,5,6,8
Gal 4:4-7
Lk 2:16-21

Friday, January 2

STS. BASIL THE GREAT AND GREGORY NAZIANZEN,
BISHOPS AND DOCTORS *(White)*

"Remain in union with [Christ] so that when He appears we may be full of courage and need not hide in shame from Him on the Day He comes." (1 Jn 2:28)

1 Jn 2:22-28
Ps 98:1-4
Jn 1:19-28

Saturday, January 3

THE MOST HOLY NAME OF JESUS *(White)*

"[The Father's] love is so great that we are called God's children — and so, in fact, we are." (1 Jn 3:1b)

1 Jn 2:29—3:6
Ps 98:1,3-6
Jn 1:29-34

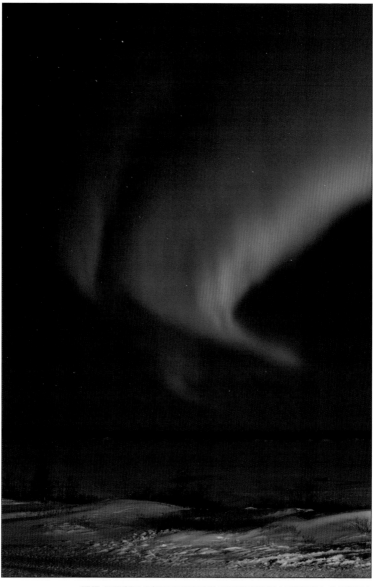

THE AURORA BOREALIS OVER NORTHERN MANITOBA, CANADA

"God, who is love, showed Himself, a Child. [The Magi] took love away and returned whence they came. And as they went, they became lights, because they burned with love."

from *Dear Parents: A Gift of Love for Families*

Sunday, January 4

EPIPHANY OF THE LORD *(White)*

"...on you the light of the LORD will shine; the brightness of His presence will be with you." (Is 60:2bc)

Is 60:1-6
Ps 72:1-2,7-8,10-11,12-13
Eph 3:2-3a,5-6
Mt 2:1-12

Monday, January 5

ST. JOHN NEUMANN, BISHOP *(White)*

"...the Spirit who is in you is more powerful than the spirit in those who belong to the world." (1 Jn 4:4b)

1 Jn 3:22—4:6
Ps 2:7-8,10-11
Mt 4:12-17,23-25

Tuesday, January 6

BLESSED ANDRÉ BESSETTE, RELIGIOUS *(White)*

"Let us love one another, because love comes from God." (1 Jn 4:7)

1 Jn 4:7-10
Ps 72:1-4,7-8
Mk 6:34-44

Wednesday, January 7

ST. RAYMOND OF PENYAFORT, PRIEST *(White)*

"God is love, and those who live in love live in union with God and God lives in union with them." (1 Jn 4:16b)

1 Jn 4:11-18
Ps 72:1-2,10,12-13
Mk 6:45-52

Thursday, January 8

CHRISTMAS WEEKDAY *(White)*

"We love God because God first loved us." (1 Jn 4:19)

1 Jn 4:19—5:4
Ps 72:1-2,14-15,17
Lk 4:14-22a

Friday, January 9

CHRISTMAS WEEKDAY *(White)*

"God has given us eternal life, and this life has its source in His Son. Whoever has the Son has this life." (1 Jn 5:11-12a)

1 Jn 5:5-13
Ps 147:12-15,19-20
Lk 5:12-16

Saturday, January 10

CHRISTMAS WEEKDAY *(White)*

"No one can have anything unless God gives it." (Jn 3:27)

1 Jn 5:14-21
Ps 149:1-6,9
Jn 3:22-30

GLACIER NATIONAL PARK, MONTANA

"In the sacrament of Baptism, love becomes a love letter from Christ to the person being baptized. What boundless love!"

from *Living the Gospel Without Compromise*

Sunday, January 11

THE BAPTISM OF THE LORD *(White)*

"...every child of God is able to defeat the world...by means of our faith." (1 Jn 5:4)

Is 42:1-4,6-7 or Is 55:1-11
Ps 29:1-4,9-10
Acts 10:34-38 or 1 Jn 5:1-9
Mk 1:7-11

Monday, January 12

WEEKDAY *(Green) - 1st Week in Ordinary Time*
CANADA: ST. MARGUERITE BOURGEOYS, VIRGIN *(White)*

"'The right time has come,' [Jesus] said, '...turn away from your sins and believe the Good News!'" (Mk 1:15)

Heb 1:1-6
Ps 97:1-2,6-7,9
Mk 1:14-20

Tuesday, January 13

WEEKDAY *(Green)*   ST. HILARY, BISHOP AND DOCTOR *(White)*

"The people who heard [Jesus] were amazed at the way He taught, for...He taught with authority." (Mk 1:22)

Heb 2:5-12
Ps 8:2,5,6-9
Mk 1:21-28

Wednesday, January 14

WEEKDAY *(Green)*

"Jesus healed many who were sick with all kinds
of diseases and drove out many demons."
(Mk 1:34)

Heb 2:14-18
Ps 105:1-4,6-9
Mk 1:29-39

Thursday, January 15

WEEKDAY *(Green)*

"Be careful that none of you have a heart so evil
and unbelieving that you will turn away from
the living God." (Heb 3:12)

Heb 3:7-14
Ps 95:6-11
Mk 1:40-45

Friday, January 16

WEEKDAY *(Green)*

"We will tell the next generation about the
LORD's power and His great deeds..." (Ps 78:4b)

Heb 4:1-5,11
Ps 78:3-4,6-8
Mk 2:1-12

Saturday, January 17

ST. ANTHONY, ABBOT *(White)*

"There is nothing that can be hid from God."
(Heb 4:13a)

Heb 4:12-16
Ps 19:8-10,15
Mk 2:13-17

A ROCKY MOUNTAIN GOAT IN GLACIER NATIONAL PARK, MONTANA

"We remember that Christ walked the earth. Step by step, walking with Him, believing that He is the first person in whom we should confide, we walk with Him in faith and in trust, and we tell Him our problems."

from *On the Cross of Rejection: Meditations—when your heart is pierced*

Sunday, January 18

SECOND SUNDAY IN ORDINARY TIME *(Green)*
WEEK OF PRAYER FOR CHRISTIAN UNITY BEGINS

"Speak, LORD, Your servant is listening."
(1 Sam 3:9a)

1 Sam 3:3b-10,19
Ps 40:2,4,7-10
1 Cor 6:13c-15a,17-20
Jn 1:35-42

Monday, January 19 MARTIN LUTHER KING DAY

WEEKDAY *(Green)*

"When [Jesus] was made perfect [in obedience],
He became the source of eternal salvation for all
those who obey Him." (Heb 5:9)

Heb 5:1-10
Ps 110:1-4
Mk 2:18-22

Tuesday, January 20

WEEKDAY *(Green)*   ST. FABIAN, POPE AND MARTYR *(Red)*
ST. SEBASTIAN, MARTYR *(Red)*

"...be like those who believe and are patient, and
so receive what God has promised." (Heb 6:12b)

Heb 6:10-20
Ps 111:1-2,4-5,9-10
Mk 2:23-28

Wednesday, January 21

ST. AGNES, VIRGIN AND MARTYR *(Red)*

"Jesus was angry...but at the same time felt sorry for [the people], because they were so stubborn and wrong." (Mk 3:5)

Heb 7:1-3,15-17
Ps 110:1-4
Mk 3:1-6

Thursday, January 22

WEEKDAY *(Green)*
*DAY OF PRAYER FOR THE LEGAL PROTECTION
    OF UNBORN CHILDREN (White or Violet)*

"...LORD, I told the good news that You save us... I will never stop telling it." (Ps 40:9)

Heb 7:25—8:6
Ps 40:7-10,17
Mk 3:7-12
Readings for the Day of Prayer: see Appendix

Friday, January 23

WEEKDAY *(Green)*   ST. VINCENT, DEACON AND MARTYR *(Red)*
ST. MARIANNE COPE, VIRGIN *(White)*

"[God]...promises peace to us...if we do not go
back to our foolish ways." (Ps 85:8)

Heb 8:6-13
Ps 85:8,10-14
Mk 3:13-19

Saturday, January 24

ST. FRANCIS DE SALES, BISHOP AND DOCTOR *(White)*

"Sing praise to God; sing praise to our king!"
(Ps 47:6)

Heb 9:2-3,11-14
Ps 47:2-3,6-7,8-9
Mk 3:20-21

POLAR BEARS IN NORTHERN MANITOBA, CANADA

"Sanctity comes from much loving. For this we have been created: to love our neighbor, and through him, to love God. Loving is fun. Loving is joy. Loving brings peace. Loving means serving and forgetting oneself for others. Learn how to love and you will receive everything you need."

from *God in the Nitty-Gritty Life*

Sunday, January 25

THIRD SUNDAY IN ORDINARY TIME *(Green)*

"God saw...that [the Ninevites] had given up
their wicked behavior. So He changed His mind
and did not punish them..." (Jon 3:10)

Jon 3:1-5,10
Ps 25:4-9
1 Cor 7:29-31
Mk 1:14-20

Monday, January 26

STS. TIMOTHY AND TITUS, BISHOPS *(White)*

"The Spirit that God has given us...fills us with power, love and self-control." (2 Tm 1:7)

2 Tm 1:1-8 or Ti 1:1-5
Ps 89:20-22,25-26
Mk 3:22-30

Tuesday, January 27

WEEKDAY *(Green)*   ST. ANGELA MERICI, VIRGIN *(White)*

"...we are all purified from sin by the offering that [Jesus] made of His own body once and for all." (Heb 10:10b)

Heb 10:1-10
Ps 40:2,4,7-8,10-11
Mk 3:31-35

Wednesday, January 28

ST. THOMAS AQUINAS, PRIEST AND DOCTOR *(White)*

"Christ...offered one sacrifice for sins, an offering
that is effective forever..." (Heb 10:12a)

Heb 10:11-18
Ps 110:1-4
Mk 4:1-20

Thursday, January 29

WEEKDAY *(Green)*

"[Jesus said]... 'The same rules you use to judge
others will be used by God to judge you...'"
(Mk 4:24)

Heb 10:19-25
Ps 24:1-6
Mk 4:21-25

Friday, January 30

WEEKDAY *(Green)*

"You need to be patient, in order to do the will of God and receive what He promises." (Heb 10:36)

Heb 10:32-39
Ps 37:3-6,23-24,39-40
Mk 4:26-34

Saturday, January 31

ST. JOHN BOSCO, PRIEST *(White)*

"To have faith is to be sure of the things we hope for, to be certain of the things we cannot see." (Heb 11:1)

Heb 11:1-2,8-19
(Ps) Lk 1:69-75
Mk 4:35-41

A GREAT HORNED OWL NEAR ELY, MINNESOTA

"[S]in means 'forgetting' in Hebrew. It's a very good definition of sin... Sin means forgetting God—separating from Him, turning our backs toward Him."

from *Beginning Again: Recovering your innocence and joy through Confession*

Sunday, February 1

FOURTH SUNDAY IN ORDINARY TIME *(Green)*

"...do what is right and proper, and...give
yourselves completely to the Lord's service..."
(1 Cor 7:35c)

Dt 18:15-20
Ps 95:1-2,6-9
1 Cor 7:32-35
Mk 1:21-28

Monday, February 2

THE PRESENTATION OF THE LORD *(White)*

"Jesus Himself became [like all the children of God] and shared their human nature...so that through His death He might destroy the Devil..." (Heb 2:14)

Mal 3:1-4
Ps 24:7-10
Heb 2:14-18
Lk 2:22-40

Tuesday, February 3

WEEKDAY *(Green)*   ST. BLASE, BISHOP AND MARTYR *(Red)*
ST. ANSGAR, BISHOP *(White)*

"For [unlike Christ], in your struggle against sin, you have not yet had to resist to the point of being killed." (Heb 12:4)

Heb 12:1-4
Ps 22:26-28,30-32
Mk 5:21-43

Wednesday, February 4

WEEKDAY *(Green)*

"Keep walking on straight paths, so that the
lame foot may not be disabled, but instead be
healed." (Heb 12:13)

Heb 12:4-7,11-15
Ps 103:1-2,13-14,17-18
Mk 6:1-6

Thursday, February 5

ST. AGATHA, VIRGIN AND MARTYR *(Red)*

"You rule with justice, [O God]... You give right
judgments." (Ps 48:10c,11b)

Heb 12:18-19,21-24
Ps 48:2-4,9-11
Mk 6:7-13

Friday, February 6

ST. PAUL MIKI, PRIEST AND MARTYR,
AND HIS COMPANIONS, MARTYRS *(Red)*

"Marriage is to be honored by all, and husbands
and wives must be faithful to each other."
(Heb 13:4)

Heb 13:1-8
Ps 27:1,3,5,8-9
Mk 6:14-29

Saturday, February 7

WEEKDAY *(Green)*   BLESSED VIRGIN MARY *(White)*

"May [God], through Jesus Christ, do in us what
pleases Him." (Heb 13:21)

Heb 13:15-17,20-21
Ps 23:1-6
Mk 6:30-34

AN ARCTIC FOX IN NORTHERN MANITOBA, CANADA

"You have to listen very carefully because the footsteps of God are very soft, like a whisper."

from *Dear Parents: A Gift of Love for Families*

Sunday, February 8

FIFTH SUNDAY IN ORDINARY TIME *(Green)*

"Remember, O God, my life is only a breath..."
(Job 7:7a)

Job 7:1-4,6-7
Ps 147:1-6
1 Cor 9:16-19,22-23
Mk 1:29-39

Monday, February 9

WEEKDAY *(Green)*

"In the beginning...God created the universe."
(Gen 1:1)

Gen 1:1-19
Ps 104:1-2,5-6,10,12,24,35
Mk 6:53-56

Tuesday, February 10

ST. SCHOLASTICA, VIRGIN *(White)*

"Jesus [said to the Pharisees], 'You have a clever
way of rejecting God's law in order to uphold
your own teaching.'" (Mk 7:9)

Gen 1:20—2:4a
Ps 8:4-9
Mk 7:1-13

Wednesday, February 11

WEEKDAY *(Green)*   OUR LADY OF LOURDES *(White)*

"...from your heart come the evil ideas which lead you to do immoral things..." (Mk 7:21)

Gen 2:4b-9,15-17
Ps 104:1-2,27-30
Mk 7:14-23

Thursday, February 12

WEEKDAY *(Green)*

"...a man leaves his father and mother and is united with his wife, and they become one." (Gen 2:24)

Gen 2:18-25
Ps 128:1-5
Mk 7:24-30

Friday, February 13

WEEKDAY *(Green)*

"You are my hiding place, [O LORD]; You will
save me from trouble." (Ps 32:7)

Gen 3:1-8
Ps 32:1-2,5-7
Mk 7:31-37

Saturday, February 14 VALENTINE'S DAY

STS. CYRIL, MONK, AND METHODIUS, BISHOP *(White)*

"Teach us how short our life is, [O LORD], so that
we may become wise." (Ps 90:12)

Gen 3:9-24
Ps 90:2-6,12-13
Mk 8:1-10

DIAMONDBACK RATTLESNAKE IN SOUTHERN ARIZONA

"If we have faith in God, we must have faith in men. Even the most evil among us has some redeeming feature. Faith will seek it out."

from *Poustinia: Encountering God in Silence, Solitude and Prayer*

Sunday, February 15

SIXTH SUNDAY IN ORDINARY TIME *(Green)*

"Whatever you do ...do it all for God's glory."
(1 Cor 10:31)

Lv 13:1-2,44-46
Ps 32:1-2,5-11
1 Cor 10:31—11:1
Mk 1:40-45

Monday, February 16

WEEKDAY *(Green)*

"...sin is crouching at your door. It wants to rule
you, but you must overcome it." (Gen 4:7)

Gen 4:1-15,25
Ps 50:1,8,16-17,20-21
Mk 8:11-13

Tuesday, February 17

WEEKDAY *(Green)*
THE SEVEN HOLY FOUNDERS OF THE SERVITE ORDER, RELIGIOUS *(White)*

"Praise the LORD ...praise His glory and power."
(Ps 29:1)

Gen 6:5-8; 7:1-5,10
Ps 29:1-4,9-10
Mk 8:14-21

Wednesday, February 18

ASH WEDNESDAY *(Violet)*

"Come back to the LORD your God... He is always ready to forgive and not punish." (Jl 2:13)

Jl 2:12-18
Ps 51:3-6,12-14,17
2 Cor 5:20—6:2
Mt 6:1-6,16-18

Thursday, February 19

THURSDAY AFTER ASH WEDNESDAY *(Violet)*

"I am now giving you the choice between life and death, between God's blessing and God's curse... Choose life." (Dt 30:19)

Dt 30:15-20
Ps 1:1-4,6
Lk 9:22-25

Friday, February 20

FRIDAY AFTER ASH WEDNESDAY *(Violet)*

"When you pray, I will answer you... if you put an end to oppression, to every gesture of contempt, and to every evil word." (Is 58:9a)

Is 58:1-9a
Ps 51:3-6,18-19
Mt 9:14-15

Saturday, February 21

SATURDAY AFTER ASH WEDNESDAY *(Violet)*
ST. PETER DAMIAN, BISHOP AND DOCTOR *(Violet for Lent)*

"Save me, for I am Your servant and I trust in You, [O LORD]." (Ps 86:2)

Is 58:9b-14
Ps 86:1-6
Lk 5:27-32

GREAT DIAMOND LAKE IN MANITOBA, CANADA

"Let us truly join hands in deep forgiveness of one another. Let us reconcile ourselves to anyone with whom we are not yet reconciled. Let us forget any attachment to anything that isn't God. Let us enlarge the circle of love in our heart, so that it can encompass humanity."

from *Marriage: A Fountain of Grace*

Sunday, February 22

FIRST SUNDAY OF LENT *(Violet)*

"[Baptism] saves you through the resurrection of Jesus Christ, who has gone to heaven and is at the right side of God, ruling over all angels and heavenly authorities and powers." (1 Pt 3:21c-22)

Gen 9:8-15
Ps 25:4-9
1 Pt 3:18-22
Mk 1:12-15

Monday, February 23

LENTEN WEEKDAY *(Violet)*
ST. POLYCARP, BISHOP AND MARTYR *(Violet for Lent)*

"Be holy, because I, the LORD your God, am holy."
(Lv 19:2)

Lv 19:1-2,11-18
Ps 19:8-10,15
Mt 25:31-46

Tuesday, February 24

LENTEN WEEKDAY *(Violet)*

"If you forgive others the wrongs they have done
to you, your Father in heaven will also forgive
you." (Mt 6:14)

Is 55:10-11
Ps 34:4-7,16-19
Mt 6:7-15

Wednesday, February 25

LENTEN WEEKDAY *(Violet)*

"Everyone must pray earnestly to God and give
up his wicked behavior and his evil actions."
(Jon 3:8)

Jon 3:1-10
Ps 51:3-4,12-13,18-19
Lk 11:29-32

Thursday, February 26

LENTEN WEEKDAY *(Violet)*

"Ask and you will receive; seek and you will
find; knock and the door will be opened to you."
(Mt 7:7)

Est C:12,14-16,23-25
Ps 138:1-3,7-8
Mt 7:7-12

Friday, February 27

LENTEN WEEKDAY *(Violet)*

"When someone evil stops sinning and does
what is right and good, he saves his life."
(Ez 18:27)

Ez 18:21-28
Ps 130:1-8
Mt 5:20-26

Saturday, February 28

LENTEN WEEKDAY *(Violet)*

"Today the LORD your God commands you to
obey all His laws; so obey them faithfully with
all your heart." (Dt 26:16)

Dt 26:16-19
Ps 119:1-2,4-5,7-8
Mt 5:43-48

A CARDINAL IN SOUTHERN ARIZONA

"Because sinning means forgetting God, repentance means a turning around, doing what I know I must do. Repentance is the incarnation of the gospel in a person's life. To repent is to change, it is not just to acknowledge that I have done wrong. It is to turn my back to the wrong and start doing right..."

from *Living the Gospel Without Compromise*

Sunday, March 1

SECOND SUNDAY OF LENT *(Violet)*

"[God] gave us His Son—will He not also freely give us all things?" (Rom 8:32b)

Gen 22:1-2,9a,10-13,15-18
Ps 116:10,15-19
Rom 8:31b-34
Mk 9:2-10

Monday, March 2

EASTER WEEKDAY *(White)*

"The measure [of generosity] you use for others is the one that God will use for you." (Lk 6:38c)

Dan 9:4b-10
Ps 79:8-9,11,13
Lk 6:36-38

Tuesday, March 3

LENTEN WEEKDAY *(Violet)*
ST. KATHARINE DREXEL, VIRGIN *(Violet for Lent)*

"Wash yourselves clean. Yes, stop doing evil and learn to do right. See that justice is done—help those who are oppressed..." (Is 1:16-17)

Is 1:10,16-20
Ps 50:8-9,16-17,21,23
Mt 23:1-12

Wednesday, March 4

LENTEN WEEKDAY *(Violet)*   ST. CASIMIR *(Violet for Lent)*

"My trust is in You, O LORD; You are my God.
I am always in Your care." (Ps 31:14-15a)

Jer 18:18-20
Ps 31:5-6,14-16
Mt 20:17-28

Thursday, March 5

LENTEN WEEKDAY *(Violet)*

"Happy are those who...do not follow the
example of sinners or join those who have
no use for God." (Ps 1:1)

Jer 17:5-10
Ps 1:1-4,6
Lk 16:19-31

Friday, March 6

LENTEN WEEKDAY *(Violet)*

"The Kingdom of God will be taken away from [those who reject it] and given to...people who will produce the proper fruits." (Mt 21:43)

Gen 37:3-4,12-13a,17b-28a
Ps 105:16-21
Mt 21:33-43,45-46

Saturday, March 7

LENTEN WEEKDAY *(Violet)*
STS. PERPETUA AND FELICITY, MARTYRS *(Violet for Lent)*

"You, [O Lord], will be merciful to us once again. You will trample our sins underfoot and send them to the bottom of the sea!" (Mi 7:19)

Mi 7:14-15,18-20
Ps 103:1-4,9-12
Lk 15:1-3,11-32

MONUMENT VALLEY, ARIZONA

"God loves me. He loves me when I am good and when I am not so good, because He loves sinners. He forgives them, too. God's mercy is infinite, and so is His love, His goodness and His forgiveness. What a consoling thought this is."

from *Beginning Again: Recovering your innocence and joy through Confession*

Sunday, March 8 *Daylight Savings Time Begins*

THIRD SUNDAY OF LENT *(Violet)*

"We proclaim the crucified Christ...who is the power of God and the wisdom of God."
(1 Cor 1:23a,24)

Ex 20:1-17
Ps 19:8-11
1 Cor 1:22-25
Jn 2:13-25

Monday, March 9

LENTEN WEEKDAY *(Violet)*
ST. FRANCES OF ROME, WIFE, MOTHER, RELIGIOUS *(Violet for Lent)*

"Send Your light and Your truth, [O God]; may
they lead me..." (Ps 43:3)

2 Kgs 5:1-15b
Ps 42:2-3; 43:3-4
Lk 4:24-30

Tuesday, March 10

LENTEN WEEKDAY *(Violet)*

"Now with all our hearts we promise to obey
You, worship You, and come to You in prayer,
[O Lord our God]." (Dan 3:41)

Dan 3:25,34-43
Ps 25:4-9
Mt 18:21-35

Wednesday, March 11

LENTEN WEEKDAY *(Violet)*

"Remember that as long as heaven and earth last, not the...smallest detail of the Law will be done away with..." (Mt 5:18)

Dt 4:1,5-9
Ps 147:12-13,15-16,19-20
Mt 5:17-19

Thursday, March 12

LENTEN WEEKDAY *(Violet)*

"Listen today to what [the LORD] says, 'Don't be stubborn...'" (Ps 95:7d-8a)

Jer 7:23-28
Ps 95:1-2,6-9
Lk 11:14-23

Friday, March 13

LENTEN WEEKDAY *(Violet)*

"Return...and let this prayer be your offering to
[the LORD]: 'Forgive all our sins, accept our
prayer, and we will praise You...'" (Hos 14:2)

Hos 14:2-10
Ps 81:6-11,14,17
Mk 12:28-34

Saturday, March 14

LENTEN WEEKDAY *(Violet)*

"[The LORD] will come to us as surely as the day
dawns, as surely as the spring rains fall upon the
earth." (Hos 6:3)

Hos 6:1-6
Ps 51:3-4,18-21
Lk 18:9-14

PRAYERTOWN EMMANUEL NEAR AMARILLO, TEXAS

"Lent brings with it Calvary. Let us, then, arise and walk every step of these Lenten days until, standing with Mary under Christ's cross, we begin to love Him back as He should be loved, and by that very loving, restore His kingdom to Him."

from *Dear Parents: A Gift of Love for Families*

Sunday, March 15

FOURTH SUNDAY OF LENT *(Violet or Rose)*

"God has made us what we are, and in our union with Christ Jesus, He has created us for a life of good deeds, which He has already prepared for us to do." (Eph 2:10)

2 Chr 36:14-16,19-23
Ps 137:1-2,3,4-5,6
Eph 2:4-10
Jn 3:14-21

Monday, March 16

LENTEN WEEKDAY *(Violet)*

"I [the LORD] am making a new earth and new heavens. The events of the past will be completely forgotten." (Is 65:17)

Is 65:17-21
Ps 30:2,4-6,11-13
Jn 4:43-54

Tuesday, March 17

LENTEN WEEKDAY *(Violet)*   ST. PATRICK, BISHOP *(Violet for Lent)*

"We will not be afraid, even if the earth is shaken and mountains fall into the ocean depths." (Ps 46:2)

Ez 47:1-9,12
Ps 46:2-3,5-6,8-9
Jn 5:1-16

Wednesday, March 18

LENTEN WEEKDAY *(Violet)*
ST. CYRIL OF JERUSALEM, BISHOP AND DOCTOR *(Violet for Lent)*

"Even if a mother should forget her child, I [God] will never forget you." (Is 49:15b)

Is 49:8-15
Ps 145:8-9,13-14,17-18
Jn 5:17-30

Thursday, March 19

ST JOSEPH, SPOUSE OF THE BLESSED VIRGIN MARY *(White)*
Patronal Feastday of Canada

"'Joseph,' [the angel said], '...do not be afraid to take Mary to be your wife... She will have a son, and you will name Him Jesus...'" (Mt 1:20,21)

2 Sam 7:4-5a,12-14a,16
Ps 89:2-5,27-29
Rom 4:13,16-18,22
Mt 1:16,18-21,24a or Lk 2:41-51a

Friday, March 20

LENTEN WEEKDAY *(Violet)*

"The LORD is near to those who are discouraged; He saves those who have lost all hope." (Ps 34:19)

Wis 2:1a,12-22
Ps 34:17-21,23
Jn 7:1-2,10,25-30

Saturday, March 21

LENTEN WEEKDAY *(Violet)*

"God is my protector; He saves those who obey Him." (Ps 7:10)

Jer 11:18-20
Ps 7:2-3,9-12
Jn 7:40-53

A WILDFLOWER IN YELLOWSTONE NATIONAL PARK, WYOMING

"After confession of sin, guilt should be totally alien to the Christian who has faith. Faith permits us to know the mercy of God."

from *Re-Entry into Faith: "Courage—be not afraid!"*

Sunday, March 22

FIFTH SUNDAY OF LENT *(Violet)*

"Even though He was God's Son, [Jesus] learned through His sufferings to be obedient. When He was made perfect, He became the source of eternal salvation for all those who obey Him." (Heb 5:8-9)

Jer 31:31-34
Ps 51:3-4,12-15
Heb 5:7-9
Jn 12:20-33

Monday, March 23

LENTEN WEEKDAY *(Violet)*
ST. TORIBIUS OF MOGROVEJO, BISHOP *(Violet for Lent)*

"Jesus said, 'I do not condemn you either. Go, but do not sin again.'" (Jn 8:11)

Dan 13:1-9,15-17,19-30,33-62
Ps 23:1-6
Jn 8:1-11

Tuesday, March 24

LENTEN WEEKDAY *(Violet)*

"When I am in trouble, [LORD], don't turn away from me! Listen...and answer me quickly when I call!" (Ps 102:2)

Num 21:4-9
Ps 102:2-3,16-21
Jn 8:21-30

Wednesday, March 25

THE ANNUNCIATION OF THE LORD *(White)*

"Here I am to do Your will, O God..." (Heb 10:7a)

Is 7:10-14; 8:10
Ps 40:7-11
Heb 10:4-10
Lk 1:26-38

Thursday, March 26

LENTEN WEEKDAY *(Violet)*

"[Jesus told them], 'Whoever obeys My teaching will never die.'" (Jn 8:51)

Gen 17:3-9
Ps 105:4-9
Jn 8:51-59

Friday, March 27

LENTEN WEEKDAY *(Violet)*

"My God is my protection, and with Him I am safe." (Ps 18:2b)

Jer 20:10-13
Ps 18:2-7
Jn 10:31-42

Saturday, March 28

LENTEN WEEKDAY *(Violet)*

"[The LORD says], 'I will comfort [My people] and turn their mourning into joy, their sorrow into gladness.'" (Jer 31:13c)

Ez 37:21-28
(Ps) Jer 31:10-13
Jn 11:45-56

SAGUARO CACTI IN SAGUARO NATIONAL PARK, ARIZONA

"I cannot visualize a love story with God without a cross. To me the cross is *the thing!* I desire it. I accept it. And I ask the grace never to fear it, because at the end, I shall know its joy."

from *Grace in Every Season: Through the Year with Catherine Doherty*

Sunday, March 29

PALM SUNDAY OF THE PASSION OF THE LORD *(Red)*

"All beings...will fall on their knees and...openly proclaim that Jesus Christ is Lord, to the glory of God the Father." (Phil 2:10-11)

Mk 11:1-10 or Jn 12:12-16
Is 50:4-7
Ps 22:8-9,17-20,23-24
Phil 2:6-11
Mk 14:1—15:47

Monday, March 30

MONDAY OF HOLY WEEK *(Violet)*

"The LORD is my light and my salvation; I will fear no one." (Ps 27:1a)

Is 42:1-7
Ps 27:1-3,13-14
Jn 12:1-11

Tuesday, March 31

TUESDAY OF HOLY WEEK *(Violet)*

"Now the Son of Man's glory is revealed; now God's glory is revealed through Him." (Jn 13:31)

Is 49:1-6
Ps 71:1-6,15,17
Jn 13:21-33,36-38

Wednesday, April 1

WEDNESDAY OF HOLY WEEK *(Violet)*

"Every morning [the Sovereign LORD] makes me
eager to hear what He is going to teach me."
(Is 50:4b)

Is 50:4-9a
Ps 69:8-10,21-22,31,33-34
Mt 26:14-25

Thursday, April 2   HOLY THURSDAY

THURSDAY OF THE LORD'S SUPPER *(White)*

"[Jesus told them], 'This cup is God's new
covenant, sealed with My blood. Whenever you
drink it, do so in memory of Me.'" (1 Cor 11:25)

Chrism Mass *(White)*
Is 61:1-3a,6a,8b-9
Ps 89:21-22,25,27
Rv 1:5-8
Lk 4:16-21

Mass of the Lord's Supper *(White)*
Ex 12:1-8,11-14
Ps 116:12-13,15-18
1 Cor 11:23-26
Jn 13:1-15

Friday, April 3 GOOD FRIDAY

FRIDAY OF THE PASSION OF THE LORD *(Red)*

"[The Suffering Servant] took the place of many
sinners and prayed that they might be forgiven."
(Is 53:12b)

Is 52:13—53:12
Ps 31:2,6,12-13,15-17,25
Heb 4:14-16; 5:7-9
Jn 18:1—19:42

Saturday, April 4 HOLY SATURDAY

EASTER VIGIL *(White)*

"Since we have died with Christ [through
baptism], we believe that we will also live
with Him." (Rom 6:8)

Easter Vigil Readings: see Appendix

SLOT CANYONS IN ARIZONA

"Alleluia! Alleluia! The Lord is risen! Alleluia! The Feast of Feasts has come! The work of salvation is accomplished!"

from *Dear Parents: A Gift of Love for Families*

Sunday, April 5 <small>EASTER</small>

EASTER SUNDAY OF THE RESURRECTION OF THE LORD *(White)*

"You have been raised to life with Christ, so set your hearts on the things that are in heaven, where Christ sits on His throne at the right side of God." (Col 3:1)

Acts 10:34a,37-43
Ps 118:1-2,16-17,22-23
Col 3:1-4 or 1 Cor 5:6b-8
Jn 20:1-9 or Mk 16:1-7

Monday, April 6

MONDAY WITHIN THE OCTAVE OF EASTER *(White)*

"You, [LORD], will show me the path that leads to life; Your presence fills me with joy and brings me pleasure forever." (Ps 16:11)

Acts 2:14,22-33
Ps 16:1-2,5,7-11
Mt 28:8-15

Tuesday, April 7

TUESDAY WITHIN THE OCTAVE OF EASTER *(White)*

"Each one of you must turn away from your sins and be baptized...and you will receive God's gift, the Holy Spirit." (Acts 2:38)

Acts 2:36-41
Ps 33:4-5,18-20,22
Jn 20:11-18

Wednesday, April 8

WEDNESDAY WITHIN THE OCTAVE OF EASTER *(White)*

"[Jesus] sat down to eat with them, took the bread, said the blessing...broke...and gave it to them. Then...they recognized Him." (Lk 24:30-31)

Acts 3:1-10
Ps 105:1-4,6-9
Lk 24:13-35

Thursday, April 9

THURSDAY WITHIN THE OCTAVE OF EASTER *(White)*

"O LORD, our Lord, Your greatness is seen in all the world!" (Ps 8:9)

Acts 3:11-26
Ps 8:2-9
Lk 24:35-48

Friday, April 10

FRIDAY WITHIN THE OCTAVE OF EASTER *(White)*

"Salvation is to be found through [Jesus Christ] alone; in all the world there is no one else whom God has given who can save us." (Acts 4:12)

Acts 4:1-12
Ps 118:1-2,4,22-27
Jn 21:1-14

Saturday, April 11

SATURDAY WITHIN THE OCTAVE OF EASTER *(White)*

"'Whoever believes [in the gospel] and is baptized will be saved,' [Jesus said]." (Mk 16:15)

Acts 4:13-21
Ps 118:1,14-21
Mk 16:9-15

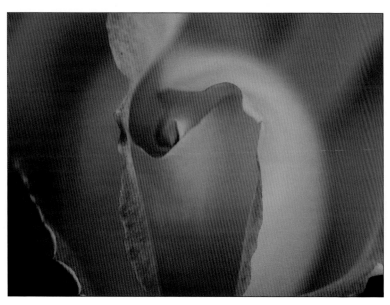

A ROSE IN NORTHEASTERN ILLINOIS

"To me the judgment of Christ is mercy and tenderness and gentleness, and I have never had any fear of judgment, provided I say I am sorry! I would tremble in my boots if I didn't say 'I am sorry.' That's a different story!"

from *Kiss of Christ: Reflections on the Sacrament of Penance and Reconciliation*

Sunday, April 12 DIVINE MERCY SUNDAY

SECOND SUNDAY OF EASTER *(White)*

"[Jesus] breathed on [His Apostles] and said,
'Receive the Holy Spirit. If you forgive people's
sins, they are forgiven; if you do not forgive
them, they are not forgiven.'" (Jn 20:21-23)

Acts 4:32-35
Ps 118:2-4,13-15,22-24
1 Jn 5:1-6
Jn 20:19-31

Monday, April 13

EASTER WEEKDAY *(White)*   ST. MARTIN I, POPE AND MARTYR *(Red)*

"And now, Lord, ...allow us, Your servants,
to speak Your message with all boldness."
(Acts 4:29)

Acts 4:23-31
Ps 2:1-9
Jn 3:1-8

Tuesday, April 14

EASTER WEEKDAY *(White)*

"The group of believers was one in mind and
heart." (Acts 4:32a)

Acts 4:32-37
Ps 93:1-2,5
Jn 3:7b-15

Wednesday, April 15

EASTER WEEKDAY *(White)*

"God loved the world so much that He gave His only Son, so that everyone who believes in Him may not die but have eternal life." (Jn 3:16)

Acts 5:17-26
Ps 34:2-9
Jn 3:16-21

Thursday, April 16

EASTER WEEKDAY *(White)*
CANADA: ST. BERNADETTE *(White)*

"We must obey God, not men." (Acts 5:29)

Acts 5:27-33
Ps 34:2,9,17-20
Jn 3:31-36

Friday, April 17

USA: EASTER WEEKDAY *(White)*
CANADA: ST. KATERI TEKAKWITHA, VIRGIN *(White)*

"One thing only do I want: to live in the LORD's house all my life..." (Ps 27:4a)

Acts 5:34-42
Ps 27:1,4,13-14
Jn 6:1-15

Saturday, April 18

EASTER WEEKDAY *(White)*
CANADA: BLESSED MARIE-ANNE BLONDIN, VIRGIN *(White)*

"The LORD watches over those who obey Him, who trust in His constant love." (Ps 33:18)

Acts 6:1-7
Ps 33:1-2,4-5,18-19
Jn 6:16-21

AN EGRET IN EVERGLADES NATIONAL PARK, FLORIDA

"Be kind to yourself, for you are your first neighbor."

from *On the Cross of Rejection: Meditations — when your heart is pierced*

Sunday, April 19

THIRD SUNDAY OF EASTER *(White)*

"If people say that they know [the Lord] but do not obey His commands, such people are liars and there is no truth in them." (1 Jn 2:4)

Acts 3:13-15,17-19
Ps 4:2,4,7-9
1 Jn 2:1-5a
Lk 24:35-48

Monday, April 20

EASTER WEEKDAY *(White)*

"Do not work for food that spoils...[but] work for the food that lasts for eternal life...which the Son of Man will give you..." (Jn 6:27)

Acts 6:8-15
Ps 119:23-24,26-27,29-30
Jn 6:22-29

Tuesday, April 21

EASTER WEEKDAY *(White)*
ST. ANSELM, BISHOP AND DOCTOR *(White)*

"'I am the bread of life,' Jesus told them." (Jn 6:35a)

Acts 7:51—8:1a
Ps 31:3-4,6-8,17,21
Jn 6:30-35

Wednesday, April 22

EASTER WEEKDAY *(White)*

"'I will never turn away anyone who comes to Me,' [Jesus said]... 'and I will raise them up on the last day.'" (Jn 6:37b,40b)

Acts 8:1b-8
Ps 66:1-7
Jn 6:35-40

Thursday, April 23

EASTER WEEKDAY *(White)*   ST. GEORGE, MARTYR *(Red)*
ST. ADALBERT, BISHOP AND MARTYR *(Red)*

"The bread that I [Jesus] will give you is My flesh, which I give so that the world may live." (Jn 6:51b)

Acts 8:26-40
Ps 66:8-9,16-17,20
Jn 6:44-51

Friday, April 24

EASTER WEEKDAY *(White)*
ST. FIDELIS OF SIGMARINGEN, PRIEST AND MARTYR *(Red)*

"'Those who eat My flesh and drink My blood live in Me, and I live in them,' [Jesus said]." (Jn 6:56)

Acts 9:1-20
Ps 117:1-2
Jn 6:52-59

Saturday, April 25

ST. MARK, EVANGELIST *(Red)*

"God resists the proud, but shows favor to the humble." (1 Pt 5:5b)

1 Pt 5:5b-14
Ps 89:2-3,6-7,16-17
Mk 16:15-20

A SUNRISE IN MONTANA

"Awareness of little things done well for the love of God is daily living lifted up into the heart of Christ. It means we rise in the morning, aware that this day is given to us so that we may grow in grace and wisdom before the Lord."

from *God in the Nitty-Gritty Life*

Sunday, April 26

FOURTH SUNDAY OF EASTER *(White)*

"[Jesus said], 'I am the good shepherd. As the Father knows Me and I know the Father, in the same way I know My sheep and they know Me.'" (Jn 10:14-15a)

Acts 4:8-12
Ps 118:1,8-9,21-23,26,29
1 Jn 3:1-2
Jn 10:11-18

Monday, April 27

EASTER WEEKDAY *(White)*

"'I am the gate,' [Jesus told them]. 'Those who come in by Me will be saved.'" (Jn 10:9)

Acts 11:1-18
Ps 42:2-4; 43:3-4
Jn 10:1-10

Tuesday, April 28

EASTER WEEKDAY *(White)*
ST. PETER CHANEL, PRIEST AND MARTYR *(Red)*
ST. LOUIS GRIGNION DE MONTFORT, PRIEST *(White)*

"...believers...[told others] the Good News about the Lord Jesus." (Acts 11:20)

Acts 11:19-26
Ps 87:1-7
Jn 10:22-30

Wednesday, April 29

ST. CATHERINE OF SIENA, VIRGIN AND DOCTOR *(White)*

"I [Jesus] have come into the world as light, so that everyone who believes in Me should not remain in the darkness." (Jn 12:46)

Acts 12:24—13:5a
Ps 67:2-3,5-6,8
Jn 12:44-50

Thursday, April 30

EASTER WEEKDAY *(White)*   ST. PIUS V, POPE *(White)*
CANADA: BLESSED MARIE OF THE INCARNATION, RELIGIOUS *(White)*

"No slaves are greater than their master, and no messengers are greater than the one who sent them." (Jn 13:16)

Acts 13:13-25
Ps 89:2-3,21-22,25,27
Jn 13:16-20

Friday, May 1

EASTER WEEKDAY *(White)*   ST. JOSEPH THE WORKER *(White)*

"Jesus said, 'I am the way, the truth and the life.'"
(Jn 14:6)

Easter Weekday:		**St. Joseph the Worker:**
Acts 13:26-33		Gen 1:26—2:3 or Col 3:14-15,17,23-24
Ps 2:6-11	OR	Ps 90:2,3-4,12-14,16
Jn 14:1-6		Mt 13:54-58

Saturday, May 2

ST. ATHANASIUS, BISHOP AND DOCTOR *(White)*

"Sing for joy to the LORD, all the earth; praise
Him with songs and shouts of joy!" (Ps 98:4)

Acts 13:44-52
Ps 98:1-4
Jn 14:7-14

TULIPS IN NORTHEASTERN ILLINOIS

"Love alone can bring about the salvation of the world."

from *Light in the Darkness: A Christian Vision for Unstable Times*

Sunday, May 3

FIFTH SUNDAY OF EASTER *(White)*

"I [Jesus] am the vine, and you are the branches. Whoever remains in Me, and I in him, will bear much fruit; for you can do nothing without Me." (Jn 15:5)

Acts 9:26-31
Ps 22:26-28,30-32
1 Jn 3:18-24
Jn 15:1-8

Monday, May 4

EASTER WEEKDAY *(White)*
CANADA: BLESSED MARIE-LÉONIE PARADIS, RELIGIOUS *(White)*

"My Father will love those who love Me [Jesus];
I, too, will love them and reveal Myself to them."
(Jn 14:21b)

Acts 14:5-18
Ps 115:1-4,15-16
Jn 14:21-26

Tuesday, May 5

EASTER WEEKDAY *(White)*

"[Paul and Barnabas] strengthened the believers
and encouraged them to remain true to the
faith." (Acts 14:22)

Acts 14:19-28
Ps 145:10-13,21
Jn 14:27-31a

Wednesday, May 6

EASTER WEEKDAY *(White)*
CANADA: BLESSED FRANÇOIS DE MONTMORENCY-DE-LAVAL, BISHOP *(White)*

"[Jesus said], 'Remain united to Me and I will remain united to you.'" (Jn 15:4)

Acts 15:1-6
Ps 122:2-5
Jn 15:1-8

Thursday, May 7

EASTER WEEKDAY *(White)*

"We believe and are saved by the grace of the Lord Jesus..." (Acts 15:11)

Acts 15:7-21
Ps 96:1-3,10
Jn 15:9-11

Friday, May 8

EASTER WEEKDAY *(White)*
CANADA: BLESSED CATHERINE OF ST. AUGUSTINE, VIRGIN *(White)*

"[Jesus said], 'You did not choose Me; I chose you...
to go and bear much fruit...'" (Jn 15:16)

Acts 15:22-31
Ps 57:8-12
Jn 15:12-17

Saturday, May 9

EASTER WEEKDAY *(White)*

"'I chose you from this world,' [Jesus said],
'and you do not belong to it.'" (Jn 15:19)

Acts 16:1-10
Ps 100:1-3,5
Jn 15:18-21

A NESTING BROADBILLED HUMMINGBIRD IN SOUTHERN ARIZONA

"Pregnancy, an advent renewed in every woman expecting a child, is a book written by the hand of God, with each page, each day, each hour, reminding us of the first Advent."

from *Mothering: Becoming the Heart of the Home*

Sunday, May 10 <small>MOTHER'S DAY</small>

SIXTH SUNDAY OF EASTER *(White)*

"Dear friends, let us love one another, because love comes from God... Whoever does not love does not know God, for God is love." (1 Jn 4:7,8)

Acts 10:25-26,34-35,44-48
Ps 98:1-4
1 Jn 4:7-10
Jn 15:9-17

Monday, May 11

EASTER WEEKDAY *(White)*

"The LORD takes pleasure in His people; He
honors the humble with victory." (Ps 149:4)

Acts 16:11-15
Ps 149:1-6,9
Jn 15:26—16:4a

Tuesday, May 12

EASTER WEEKDAY *(White)*
STS. NEREUS AND ACHILLEUS, MARTYRS *(Red)*
ST. PANCRAS, MARTYR *(Red)*

"You answered me when I called to You, [LORD];
with Your strength You strengthened me."
(Ps 138:3)

Acts 16:22-34
Ps 138:1-3,7-8
Jn 16:5-11

Wednesday, May 13

EASTER WEEKDAY *(White)*   OUR LADY OF FATIMA *(White)*

"When...the Spirit comes, who reveals the truth about God, He will lead you into all the truth." (Jn 16:13a)

Acts 17:15,22—18:1
Ps 148:1-2,11-14
Jn 16:12-15

Thursday, May 14   *HOLY DAY OF OBLIGATION*
for relevant ecclesiastical provinces

THE ASCENSION OF THE LORD *(White)* (in some U.S. ecclesiastical provinces)
ELSEWHERE: ST. MATTHIAS, APOSTLE *(Red)*

"[Jesus said], 'Go throughout the whole world and preach the gospel to all people. Whoever believes and is baptized will be saved.'" (Mk 16:15-16a)

Acts 1:1-11
Ps 47:2-3,6-9
Eph 1:17-23 or Eph 4:1-13
Mk 16:15-20
(For the Feast of St. Matthias: Acts 1:15-17,20-26; Ps 113:1-8; Jn 15:9-17)

Friday, May 15

EASTER WEEKDAY *(White)*   ST. ISIDORE THE FARMER, HUSBAND *(White)*

"Sing praise to God; sing praise to our king!"
(Ps 47:6)

Acts 18:9-18
Ps 47:2-7
Jn 16:20-23

Saturday, May 16

EASTER WEEKDAY *(White)*

"'...the Father Himself loves you,' [Jesus said],
'...because you love Me...'" (Jn 16:27)

Acts 18:23-28
Ps 47:2-7
Jn 16:23b-28

THE SKY OVER SOUTH CAROLINA

"Let us make the glorious feast of Christ's Ascension our own, we...who need to understand in these barren, soulless days of our sterile century the blinding joy of our faith that rests in the very essence of glory—God."

from: *Dear Parents: A Gift of Love for Families*

Sunday, May 17

THE ASCENSION OF THE LORD *(White)*
in CANADA and most U.S. ecclesiastical provinces
ELSEWHERE: SEVENTH SUNDAY OF EASTER *(White)*

"This Jesus, who was taken from you into heaven, will come back in the same way that you saw Him go to heaven." (Acts 1:11)

Ascension:
Acts 1:1-11
Ps 47:2-3,6-9
Eph 1:17-23 or Eph 4:1-13
Mk 16:15-20

Seventh Sunday of Easter:
Acts 1:15-17,20a,20c-26
Ps 103:1-2,11-12,19-20
1 Jn 4:11-16
Jn 17:11b-19

Monday, May 18 <small>CANADA: VICTORIA DAY</small>

EASTER WEEKDAY *(White)*   ST. JOHN I, POPE AND MARTYR *(Red)*

"'The world will make you suffer,' [Jesus said].
'But be brave! I have defeated the world!'"
(Jn 16:33b)

Acts 19:1-8
Ps 68:2-7
Jn 16:29-33

Tuesday, May 19

EASTER WEEKDAY *(White)*

"Our God is a God who saves; He is the LORD,
our Lord, who rescues us from [eternal] death."
(Ps 68:20)

Acts 20:17-27
Ps 68:10-11,20-21
Jn 17:1-11a

Wednesday, May 20

EASTER WEEKDAY *(White)*   ST. BERNARDINE OF SIENA, PRIEST *(White)*

"[Jesus prayed], 'I gave [My followers] Your message, [Father], and the world hated them, because they do not belong to the world, just as I do not belong to the world.'" (Jn 17:14)

Acts 20:28-38
Ps 68:29-30,33-36
Jn 17:11b-19

Thursday, May 21

EASTER WEEKDAY *(White)*
ST. CHRISTOPHER MAGALLANES, PRIEST, AND COMPANIONS, MARTYRS *(Red)*
CANADA: BLESSED EUGENE DE MAZENOD, BISHOP *(White)*

"I say to the LORD, 'You are my Lord; all the good things I have come from You.'" (Ps 16:2)

Acts 22:30; 23:6-11
Ps 16:1-2,5-11
Jn 17:20-26

Friday, May 22

EASTER WEEKDAY *(White)*
ST. RITA OF CASCIA, WIFE, MOTHER, RELIGIOUS *(White)*

"As far as the east is from the west, so far does [the LORD] remove our sins from us." (Ps 103:12)

Acts 25:13b-21
Ps 103:1-2,11-12,19-20
Jn 21:15-19

Saturday, May 23

EASTER WEEKDAY *(White)*

"...[Paul] taught about the Lord Jesus Christ, speaking with all boldness and freedom." (Acts 28:31b)

Acts 28:16-20,30-31
Ps 11:4-5,7
Jn 21:20-25

THE SKY OVER MONTANA

"Gifts poured that day upon the disciples in that upper room—courage beyond the courage of men descended on them. Faith was knighted. Love became all-consuming, in a fire which they could not contain but had to rush out and share right there on the streets, with any who had ears to hear! That was the first Pentecost!"

from *Dear Parents: A Gift of Love for Families*

Sunday, May 24

PENTECOST SUNDAY *(Red)*

"There are different abilities to perform service, but the same God gives ability to all for their particular service. The Spirit's presence is shown in some way in each person for the good of all." (1 Cor 12:6-7)

Acts 2:1-11
Ps 104:1,24,29-31,34
1 Cor 12:3b-7,12-13 or Gal 5:16-25
Jn 20:19-23 or Jn 15:26-27; 16:12-15

Monday, May 25 Memorial Day

WEEKDAY *(Green)*   VENERABLE BEDE, PRIEST AND DOCTOR *(White)*
ST. GREGORY VII, POPE *(White)*
ST. MARY MAGDALENE DE PAZZI, VIRGIN *(White)*

"When we give to the poor, the Lord considers
it as precious... Human kindness is as precious
to Him as life itself." (Sir 17:22)

Sir 17:20-24
Ps 32:1-2,5-7
Mk 10:17-27

Tuesday, May 26

ST. PHILIP NERI, PRIEST *(White)*

"Give to the Most High as He has given to you,
just as generously as you can. The Lord always
repays and will do it many times over." (Sir 35:10)

Sir 35:1-12
Ps 50:5-8,14,23
Mk 10:28-31

Wednesday, May 27

WEEKDAY *(Green)*   ST. AUGUSTINE OF CANTERBURY, BISHOP *(White)*

"O Lord God of the universe, look upon us and have mercy." (Sir 36:1)

Sir 36:1,4-5a,10-17
Ps 79:8-9,11,13
Mk 10:32-45

Thursday, May 28

WEEKDAY *(Green)*

"[The Lord] sees into the oceans and into the human heart, and He knows the secrets of both." (Sir 42:18)

Sir 42:15-25
Ps 33:2-9
Mk 10:46-52

Friday, May 29

WEEKDAY *(Green)*

"'When you pray,' [Jesus told them], 'forgive anything you may have against anyone, so that your Father in heaven will forgive the wrongs you have done.'" (Mk 11:26)

Sir 44:1,9-13
Ps 149:1-2,3-4,5-6,9
Mk 11:11-26

Saturday, May 30

WEEKDAY *(Green)*   BLESSED VIRGIN MARY *(White)*

"I was determined to live wisely and was devoted to the cause of goodness. I have no regrets." (Sir 51:18)

Sir 51:12cd-20
Ps 19:8-11
Mk 11:27-33

A STRAWBERRY HEDGEHOG CACTUS IN SOUTHERN ARIZONA

"If we are...following Jesus Christ, He will take us to the Father's heart. When we are emptied of ourselves, we will be filled with the Holy Spirit... fall in love with the Most Holy Trinity, and... become part of the eternal, primary Community of Love."

from *Light in the Darkness: A Christian Vision for Unstable Times*

Sunday, May 31

THE MOST HOLY TRINITY *(White)*

"Since we are [God's] children, we will possess...
with Christ what God has kept for Him; for if we
share Christ's suffering, we will also share His
glory." (Rom 8:17)

Dt 4:32-34,39-40
Ps 33:4-6,9,18-20,22
Rom 8:14-17
Mt 28:16-20

Monday, June 1

ST. JUSTIN, MARTYR *(Red)*

"Light shines in the darkness for good people,
for those who are merciful, kind and just."
(Ps 112:4)

Tob 1:3; 2:1b-8
Ps 112:1-6
Mk 12:1-12

Tuesday, June 2

WEEKDAY *(Green)*   STS. MARCELLINUS AND PETER, MARTYRS *(Red)*

"[A good person] is not afraid of receiving bad
news; his faith is strong and he trusts in the
LORD." (Ps 112:7)

Tob 2:9-14
Ps 112:1-2,7-8,9
Mk 12:13-17

Wednesday, June 3

STS. CHARLES LWANGA AND COMPANIONS, MARTYRS *(Red)*

"You are righteous, O Lord! You are merciful in all You do, faithful in all Your ways." (Tob 3:2)

Tob 3:1-11a,16-17a
Ps 25:2-9
Mk 12:18-27

Thursday, June 4

WEEKDAY *(Green)*

"Love the Lord your God with all your heart... soul...mind and...strength." (Mk 12:30)

Tob 6:10-11; 7:1bcde,9-17; 8:4-9a
Ps 128:1-5
Mk 12:28-34

Friday, June 5

ST. BONIFACE, BISHOP AND MARTYR *(Red)*

"I will praise [the LORD] as long as I live; I will sing to my God all my life." (Ps 146:2)

Tob 11:5-17
Ps 146:2,7-10
Mk 12:35-37

Saturday, June 6

WEEKDAY *(Green)*   ST. NORBERT, BISHOP *(White)*

"Praise God and tell everyone about the good things He has done for you, so that they too will honor Him and sing His praises." (Tob 12:6)

Tob 12:1,5-15,20
(Ps) Tob 13:2,6
Mk 12:38-44

THE MOON OVER EVERGLADES NATIONAL PARK, FLORIDA

"He who eats the Bread of the Lord must in turn be 'eaten up' by others. Having received God, who is love, we must give love. We who work in the front lines of spiritual warfare know that this is the only answer for a world so desperately in search of meaning."

from *Light in the Darkness: A Christian Vision for Unstable Times*

Sunday, June 7 CORPUS CHRISTI

THE MOST HOLY BODY AND BLOOD OF CHRIST *(White)*

"While they were eating, Jesus took a piece of bread, gave a prayer of thanks, broke it and gave it to His disciples. 'Take it,' He said, 'this is My body.' Then He took a cup, gave thanks to God and handed it to them...[saying], 'This is My blood which...seals God's covenant.'" (Mk 14:22-24)

Ex 24:3-8
Ps 116:12-13,15-18
Heb 9:11-15
Mk 14:12-16,22-26

Monday, June 8

WEEKDAY *(Green)*

"Happy are those who know they are spiritually poor; the Kingdom of heaven belongs to them!" (Mt 5:3)

2 Cor 1:1-7
Ps 34:2-9
Mt 5:1-12

Tuesday, June 9

WEEKDAY *(Green)*   ST. EPHREM, DEACON AND DOCTOR *(White)*

"Your light must shine before people so that they will see the good things you do and praise your Father in heaven." (Mt 5:16)

2 Cor 1:18-22
Ps 119:129-133,135
Mt 5:13-16

Wednesday, June 10

WEEKDAY *(Green)*

"The capacity we have [to do God's work] comes from God." (2 Cor 3:5b)

2 Cor 3:4-11
Ps 99:5-9
Mt 5:17-19

Thursday, June 11

ST. BARNABAS, APOSTLE *(Red)*

"If one of you wants to be great, you must be the servant of the rest." (Mt 20:26b)

Acts 11:21b-26; 13:1-3
Ps 98:1-6
Mt 5:20-26

Friday, June 12

THE MOST SACRED HEART OF JESUS *(White)*

"I pray that Christ will make His home in your hearts through faith. I pray that you may have your roots and foundation in love." (Eph 3:17)

Hos 11:1,3-4,8c-9
(Ps) Is 12:2-6
Eph 3:8-12,14-19
Jn 19:31-37

Saturday, June 13

WEEKDAY *(Green)*
THE IMMACULATE HEART OF THE BLESSED VIRGIN MARY *(White)*
ST. ANTHONY OF PADUA, PRIEST AND DOCTOR *(White)*

"...God... through Christ changed us from enemies into His friends and gave us the task of making others His friends also." (2 Cor 5:18)

Weekday or St. Anthony:
2 Cor 5:14-21
Ps 103:1-4,8-9,11-12
Mt 5:33-37

Immaculate Heart of Mary:
Is 61:9-11
(Ps) Lk 1:46-50,53-55
Lk 2:41-51

PINE TREES NEAR SEELEY LAKE

"Yes, faith, love and hope give those who are one with Christ the strength to sharpen the lance of love...that will pierce their own heart and make a door to God for those who seek Him."

from *Sobornost: Eastern Unity of Mind and Heart for Western Man*

Sunday, June 14 <small>FLAG DAY</small>

<small>ELEVENTH SUNDAY IN ORDINARY TIME *(Green)*</small>

"All of us must appear before Christ to be judged by Him. All will receive what they deserve, according to everything they have done, good or bad, in their bodily lives." (2 Cor 5:10)

Ez 17:22-24
Ps 92:2-3,13-14,15-16
2 Cor 5:6-10
Mk 4:26-34

Monday, June 15

WEEKDAY *(Green)*

"Don't take revenge on someone who wrongs you." (Mt 5:39a)

2 Cor 6:1-10
Ps 98:1-4
Mt 5:38-42

Tuesday, June 16

WEEKDAY *(Green)*

"Love your enemies and pray for those who persecute you, so that you may become the children of your Father in heaven." (Mt 5:44-45)

2 Cor 8:1-9
Ps 146:2,5-9
Mt 5:43-48

Wednesday, June 17

WEEKDAY *(Green)*

"You should each give...not with regret or out of
a sense of duty, for God loves the one who gives
gladly." (2 Cor 9:7)

2 Cor 9:6-11
Ps 112:1-4,9
Mt 6:1-6,16-18

Thursday, June 18

WEEKDAY *(Green)*

"Our Father...may Your will be done on earth as
it is in heaven." (Mt 6:9,10)

2 Cor 11:1-11
Ps 111:1-4,7-8
Mt 6:7-15

Friday, June 19

WEEKDAY *(Green)*   ST. ROMUALD, ABBOT *(White)*

"Store up riches for yourselves in heaven... For your heart will always be where your riches are." (Mt 6:20,21)

2 Cor 11:18,21-30
Ps 34:2-7
Mt 6:19-23

Saturday, June 20

WEEKDAY *(Green)*   BLESSED VIRGIN MARY *(White)*

"Look at the birds... your Father in heaven takes care of them! Aren't you worth much more than birds?" (Mt 6:26)

2 Cor 12:1-10
Ps 34:8-13
Mt 6:24-34

BISON IN CUSTER STATE PARK, SOUTH DAKOTA

"By example, a father preaches his loudest sermons and teaches his greatest lessons. It is from his own tender, responsible actions that his children learn the heart and the art of loving."

from *Fathering: Building the New Civilization of Love*

Sunday, June 21

TWELFTH SUNDAY IN ORDINARY TIME

"Jesus...commanded the wind, 'Be quite!' and...the waves, 'Be still!' The wind died down, and there was a great calm. Then Jesus said to His disciples, 'Why are you frightened? Do you still have no faith?'" (Mk 4:39-40)

Job 38:1,8-11
Ps 107:23-26,28-31
2 Cor 5:14-17
Mk 4:35-41

Monday, June 22

WEEKDAY *(Green)*   ST. PAULINUS OF NOLA, BISHOP *(White)*
ST. JOHN FISHER, BISHOP AND MARTYR *(Red)*
ST. THOMAS MORE, HUSBAND, FATHER, MARTYR *(Red)*

"God will judge you in the same way you judge others, and He will apply to you the same rules you apply to others." (Mt 7:2)

Gen 12:1-9
Ps 33:12-13,18-20,22
Mt 7:1-5

Tuesday, June 23

WEEKDAY *(Green)*

"[Jesus said], '[T]he gate to hell is wide and... many travel it. The gate to life is narrow and the way...hard, and...few people...find it.'"
(Mt 7:13-14)

Gen 13:2,5-18
Ps 15:2-5
Mt 7:6,12-14

Wednesday, June 24

THE NATIVITY OF ST. JOHN THE BAPTIST *(White)*

"Before I was born, the LORD chose me..."
(Is 49:1b)

Is 49:1-6
Ps 139:1-3,13-15
Acts 13:22-26
Lk 1:57-66,80

Thursday, June 25

WEEKDAY *(Green)*

"Not everyone who calls Me 'Lord, Lord' will
enter the Kingdom of heaven, but only those
who do what My Father in heaven wants them
to do." (Mt 7:21)

Gen 16:1-12,15-16
Ps 106:1-5
Mt 7:21-29

Friday, June 26

WEEKDAY *(Green)*

"A man who obeys the LORD will surely be blessed..." (Ps 128:4)

Gen 17:1,9-10,15-22
Ps 128:1-5
Mt 8:1-4

Saturday, June 27

WEEKDAY *(Green)*   BLESSED VIRGIN MARY *(White)*
ST. CYRIL OF ALEXANDRIA, BISHOP AND DOCTOR *(White)*

"[Jesus made] come true what the prophet Isaiah had said, 'He himself took our sickness and carried away our diseases.'" (Mt 8:17)

Gen 18:1-15
(Ps) Lk 1:46-50,53-55
Mt 8:5-17

AFRICAN DAISIES IN NORTHEASTERN ILLINOIS

"As He was gathering His apostles, they followed Him. They could not do otherwise, for he who hears the voice of God so intimately in his heart, rises and follows Him."

from *On the Cross of Rejection: Meditations — when your heart is pierced*

Sunday, June 28

THIRTEENTH SUNDAY IN ORDINARY TIME *(Green)*

"Since you have plenty at this time, it is only fair that you should help those who are in need. Then, when you are in need and they have plenty, they will help you." (2 Cor 8:13-14)

Wis 1:13-15; 2:23-24
Ps 30:2,4-6,11-13
2 Cor 8:7,9,13-15
Mk 5:21-43

Monday, June 29

STS. PETER AND PAUL, APOSTLES *(Red)*

"[Jesus said to Peter], 'I will give you the keys of
the Kingdom of heaven; what you prohibit on earth
will be prohibited in heaven, and what you permit
on earth will be permitted in heaven.'" (Mt 16:19)

Acts 12:1-11
Ps 34:2-9
2 Tm 4:6-8,17-18
Mt 16:13-19

Tuesday, June 30

WEEKDAY *(Green)*
THE FIRST MARTYRS OF THE HOLY ROMAN CHURCH *(Red)*

"Examine me and test me, LORD, judge my
desires and thoughts." (Ps 26:2)

Gen 19:15-29
Ps 26:2-3,9-12
Mt 8:23-27

Wednesday, July 1 CANADA: CANADA DAY

WEEKDAY *(Green)*   BLESSED JUNÍPERO SERRA, PRIEST *(White)* (USA)

"Would you like to enjoy life? ...Then keep from speaking evil and from telling lies." (Ps 34:12,13)

Gen 21:5,8-20a
Ps 34:7-8,10-13
Mt 8:28-34

Thursday, July 2

WEEKDAY *(Green)*

"'Courage, My son!' [Jesus said]. 'Your sins are forgiven.'" (Mt 9:2)

Gen 22:1b-19
Ps 115:1-6,8-9
Mt 9:1-8

Friday, July 3

ST. THOMAS, APOSTLE *(Red)*

"Jesus...said, 'Peace be with you... Stop your doubting and believe.'" (Jn 20:26,27)

Eph 2:19-22
Ps 117:1-2
Jn 20:24-29

Saturday, July 4   INDEPENDENCE DAY

WEEKDAY *(Green)*   INDEPENDENCE DAY *(White)*
BLESSED VIRGIN MARY *(White)*

"Praise the LORD! Praise His name, you servants of the LORD..." (Ps 135:1)

Gen 27:1-5,15-29
Ps 135:1-6
Mt 9:14-17

SANDHILL CRANES IN BOSQUE DEL APACHE, NEW MEXICO

"Saying sorry to anybody is a beautiful thing, but to say I am sorry to God is especially beautiful. It makes you free, completely free. Try it sometime. Let that freedom enter your heart and go around saying to yourself, 'Alleluia, alleluia, alleluia!'"

from *Beginning Again: Recovering your innocence and joy through Confession*

Sunday, July 5

FOURTEENTH SUNDAY IN ORDINARY TIME *(Green)*

"I am most happy to be proud of my weaknesses, in order to feel the protection of Christ's power over me." (2 Cor 12:9b)

Ez 2:2-5
Ps 123:1-4
2 Cor 12:7-10
Mk 6:1-6a

Monday, July 6

WEEKDAY *(Green)*   ST. MARIA GORETTI, VIRGIN AND MARTYR *(Red)*

"Whoever goes to the LORD for safety...can say to Him, 'You are my defender and protector. You are my God; in You I trust.'" (Ps 91:1,2)

Gen 28:10-22a
Ps 91:1-4,14-15
Mt 9:18-26

Tuesday, July 7

WEEKDAY *(Green)*

"Pray to the Owner of the harvest that He will send out workers to gather in His harvest." (Mt 9:38)

Gen 32:23-33
Ps 17:1-3,6-8,15
Mt 9:32-38

Wednesday, July 8

WEEKDAY *(Green)*

"The LORD watches over those who obey Him,
those who trust in His constant love." (Ps 33:18)

Gen 41:55-57; 42:5-7a,17-24a
Ps 33:2-3,10-11,18-19
Mt 10:1-7

Thursday, July 9

WEEKDAY *(Green)*
ST. AUGUSTINE ZHAO RONG, PRIEST AND MARTYR,
   AND HIS COMPANIONS, CHINESE MARTYRS *(Red)*

"You received [from God] without paying, so
give without being paid." (Mt 10:8b)

Gen 44:18-21,23b-29; 45:1-5
Ps 105:16-21
Mt 10:7-15

Friday, July 10

WEEKDAY *(Green)*

"The LORD loves what is right and does not
abandon His faithful people." (Ps 37:28)

Gen 46:1-7,28-30
Ps 37:3-4,18-19,27-28,39-40
Mt 10:16-23

Saturday, July 11

ST. BENEDICT, ABBOT *(White)*

"...even the hairs of our head have all been
counted [by your heavenly Father]." (Mt 10:30)

Gen 49:29-32; 50:15-26a
Ps 105:1-4,6-7
Mt 10:24-33

A CHOLLA CACTUS IN SOUTHERN ARIZONA

"Do we face a very simple thing? That what comes out of the hands of God cannot be ugly, deformed, lousy. Now how can you have a wrong image of yourself when you know that you come from the hands of the loving God?"

from *Kiss of Christ: Reflections on the Sacrament of Penance and Reconciliation*

Sunday, July 12

FIFTEENTH SUNDAY IN ORDINARY TIME *(Green)*

"Let us praise God for His glorious grace, for the free gift He gave us in His dear Son! For by the blood of Christ, we are set free, that is, our sins are forgiven." (Eph 1:6-7a)

Am 7:12-15
Ps 85:9-14
Eph 1:3-14
Mk 6:7-13

Monday, July 13

WEEKDAY *(Green)*   ST. HENRY II, HUSBAND, EMPEROR *(White)*

"'Those who try to gain their own life will lose it,' [Jesus said]; 'but those who lose their life for My sake will gain it.'" (Mt 10:39)

Ex 1:8-14,22
Ps 124:1-8
Mt 10:34—11:1

Tuesday, July 14

WEEKDAY *(Green)*
ST. KATERI TEKAKWITHA, VIRGIN *(White)* (USA)
CANADA: ST. CAMILLUS DE LELLIS, PRIEST *(White)*

"I will praise God with a song; I will proclaim His greatness by giving Him thanks." (Ps 69:30)

Ex 2:1-15a
Ps 69:3,14,30-31,33-34
Mt 11:20-24

Wednesday, July 15

ST. BONAVENTURE, BISHOP AND DOCTOR *(White)*

"Praise the LORD, my soul!... He forgives all my sins..." (Ps 103:1a,3a)

Ex 3:1-6,9-12
Ps 103:1-4,6-7
Mt 11:25-27

Thursday, July 16

WEEKDAY *(Green)*   OUR LADY OF MOUNT CARMEL *(White)*

"Come to Me, all of you who are tired from carrying heavy loads, and I [Jesus] will give you rest." (Mt 11:28)

Ex 3:13-20
Ps 105:1,5,8-9,24-27
Mt 11:28-30

Friday, July 17

WEEKDAY *(Green)*

"I am Your servant, LORD." (Ps 116:16a)

Ex 11:10—12:14
Ps 116:12-13,15-18
Mt 12:1-8

Saturday, July 18

WEEKDAY *(Green)*   ST. CAMILLUS DE LELLIS, PRIEST *(White)* (USA)
BLESSED VIRGIN MARY *(White)*

"[God's servant] will persist until he causes
justice to triumph..." (Mt 12:20b)

Ex 12:37-42
Ps 136:1,10-15,23-24
Mt 12:14-21

A MINK KIT NEAR SANDSTONE, MINNESOTA

"We have a lousy yardstick about ourselves... the wrong image of ourselves... Our true measure is Jesus Christ—His incarnation, life, death and resurrection. You are precious."

from *On the Cross of Rejection: Meditations—when your heart is pierced*

Sunday, July 19

SIXTEENTH SUNDAY IN ORDINARY TIME *(Green)*

"Christ came and preached the Good News of peace to all..." (Eph 2:17)

Jer 23:1-6
Ps 23:1-6
Eph 2:13-18
Mk 6:30-34

Monday, July 20

WEEKDAY *(Green)*   ST. APOLLINARIUS, BISHOP AND MARTYR *(Red)*

"The LORD is my God and I will praise Him..."
(Ex 15:2b)

Ex 14:5-18
(Ps) Ex 15:1-6
Mt 12:38-42

Tuesday, July 21

WEEKDAY *(Green)*
ST. LAWRENCE OF BRINDISI, PRIEST AND DOCTOR *(White)*

"[Jesus said], 'Whoever does what My Father in
heaven wants is My brother, My sister and My
mother.'" (Mt 12:50)

Ex 14:21—15:1
(Ps) Ex 15:8-10,12,17
Mt 12:46-50

Wednesday, July 22

ST. MARY MAGDALENE, DISCIPLE OF THE LORD *(White)*

"[The Lord] gave them grain from heaven, by sending down manna for them to eat." (Ps 78:24)

Ex 16:1-5,9-15
Ps 78:18-19,23-28
Jn 20:1-2,11-18

Thursday, July 23

WEEKDAY *(Green)*
ST. BRIDGET OF SWEDEN, WIFE, MOTHER AND RELIGIOUS *(White)*

"...many prophets and many of God's people wanted...to see what you see...and to hear what you hear, but they did not." (Mt 13:17)

Ex 19:1-2,9-11,16-20b
(Ps) Dan 3:52-56
Mt 13:10-17

Friday, July 24

WEEKDAY *(Green)*   ST. SHARBEL MAKHLUF, PRIEST *(White)*

"...those who hear the [Gospel] message and understand it...bear fruit..." (Mt 13:23a)

Ex 20:1-17
Ps 19:8-11
Mt 13:18-23

Saturday, July 25

ST. JAMES, APOSTLE *(Red)*

"[The Lord's servants] are often troubled, but not crushed; sometimes in doubt, but never in despair." (2 Cor 4:8)

2 Cor 4:7-15
Ps 126:1-6
Mt 20:20-28

WILD GOOSE ISLAND IN ST. MARY LAKE IN GLACIER NATIONAL PARK, MONTANA

"You have got to approach prayer as a love affair. And the accent is not on praying; it is on the one to whom you pray... Christ absorbs you more and more and becomes the center of your life. You savor and find new depths to every word He says."

from *Light in Darkness: A Christian Vision for Unstable Times*

Sunday, July 26

SEVENTEENTH SUNDAY IN ORDINARY TIME *(Green)*

"There is one God and Father of all people, who
is Lord of all, works through all, and is in all."
(Eph 4:6)

2 Kgs 4:42-44
Ps 145:10-11,15-18
Eph 4:1-6
Jn 6:1-15

Monday, July 27

WEEKDAY *(Green)*

"The Kingdom of heaven is like...a mustard seed...
It is the smallest of all seeds, but...it becomes...a
tree, so that birds come and make their nests in its
branches." (Mt 13:31-32)

Ex 32:15-24,30-34
Ps 106:19-23
Mt 13:31-35

Tuesday, July 28

WEEKDAY *(Green)*

"As far as the east is from the west, so far does
[the LORD] remove our sins from us." (Ps 103:12)

Ex 33:7-11; 34:5b-9,28
Ps 103:6-13
Mt 13:36-43

Wednesday, July 29

ST. MARTHA, DISCIPLE OF THE LORD *(White)*

"Jesus said, '...whoever lives and believes in Me will never die. Do you believe this?'" (Jn 11:26)

Ex 34:29-35
Ps 99:5-7,9
Jn 11:19-27 or Lk 10:38-42

Thursday, July 30

WEEKDAY *(Green)*
ST. PETER CHRYSOLOGUS, BISHOP AND DOCTOR *(White)*

"How happy are those whose strength comes from You, [LORD Almighty]." (Ps 84:5a)

Ex 40:16-21,34-38
Ps 84:3-6,8,11
Mt 13:47-53

Friday, July 31

ST. IGNATIUS OF LOYOLA, PRIEST *(White)*

"I am the LORD your God... Open your mouth and I will feed you." (Ps 81:10)

Lv 23:1,4-11,15-16,27,34b-37
Ps 81:3-6,10-11
Mt 13:54-58

Saturday, August 1

ST. ALPHONSUS LIGUORI, BISHOP AND DOCTOR *(White)*

"Do not cheat [others], but obey the LORD your God." (Lv 25:17)

Lv 25:1,8-17
Ps 67:2-3,5,7-8
Mt 14:1-12

A BULL AND COW ELK IN YELLOWSTONE NATIONAL PARK, WYOMING

"If a young person enters into the holy vocation of matrimony 'to be loved,' and both partners have the same idea, then who is going to do the loving?"

from *Marriage: A Fountain of Grace*

Sunday, August 2

EIGHTEENTH SUNDAY IN ORDINARY TIME *(Green)*

"Get rid of your old self... Your hearts and minds must be made completely new, and you must put on the new self, which is created in God's likeness and reveals itself in the true life that is upright and holy." (Eph 4:22,23-24)

Ex 16:2-4,12-15
Ps 78:3-4,23-25,54
Eph 4:17,20-24
Jn 6:24-35

Monday, August 3 CANADA: CIVIC HOLIDAY

"[The LORD says]... 'How I wish My people would listen to Me; how I wish they would obey Me!'"
(Ps 81:13)

Num 11:4b-15
Ps 81:12-17
Mt 14:13-21

Tuesday, August 4

ST. JOHN VIANNEY, PRIEST *(White)*

"Remove my sin, [O God], and I will be clean; wash me and I will be whiter than snow."
(Ps 51:7)

Num 12:1-13
Ps 51:3-7,12-13
Mt 14:22-36 or 15:1-2,10-14

Wednesday, August 5

WEEKDAY *(Green)*   DEDICATION OF ST. MARY MAJOR BASILICA *(White)*
CANADA: BLESSED FRÉDÉRIC JANSOONE, PRIEST *(White)*

"We have sinned as our ancestors did... They
forgot the many times [God] showed them His
love..." (Ps 106:6a,7b)

Num 13:1-2,25—14:1,26-29a,34-35
Ps 106: 6-7,13-14,21-23
Mt 15:21-28

Thursday, August 6

THE TRANSFIGURATION OF THE LORD *(White)*

"...pay attention to [the Lord's message], because
it is like a lamp shining in a dark place until the
Day dawns and the light of the morning star
shines in your hearts." (2 Pt 1:19b)

Dan 7:9-10,13-14
Ps 97:1-2,5-6,9
2 Pt 1:16-19
Mk 9:2-10

Friday, August 7

WEEKDAY *(Green)*
ST. SIXTUS II, POPE AND MARTYR AND COMPANIONS, MARTYRS *(Red)*
ST. CAJETAN, PRIEST *(White)*

"So remember today and never forget: the LORD is God in heaven and on earth. There is no other god." (Dt 4:39)

Dt 4:32-40
Ps 77:12-16,21
Mt 16:24-28

Saturday, August 8

ST. DOMINIC, PRIEST *(White)*

"The LORD is my protector; He is my strong fortress." (Ps 18:2a)

Dt 6:4-13
Ps 18:2-4,47,51
Mt 17:14-20

A RAINBOW OVER MONARCH, MONTANA

"Perfect love casts out all fears and changes pain into joy."

from *Dear Parents: A Gift of Love for Families*

Sunday, August 9

NINETEENTH SUNDAY IN ORDINARY TIME *(Green)*

"Get rid of all bitterness, passion and anger. No more shouting or insults, no more hateful feelings of any sort. Instead, be kind and tender-hearted to one another, and forgive one another, as God has forgiven you through Christ." (Eph 4:31-32)

1 Kgs 19:4-8
Ps 34:2-9
Eph 4:30—5:2
Jn 6:41-51

Monday, August 10

ST. LAWRENCE, DEACON AND MARTYR *(Red)*

"God is able to give you more than you need, so...you will...have all you need for yourselves and more than enough for every good cause." (2 Cor 9:8)

2 Cor 9:6-10
Ps 112:1-2,5-9
Jn 12:24-26

Tuesday, August 11

ST. CLARE, VIRGIN *(White)*

"The LORD Himself will lead you and be with you. He will not fail...or abandon you, so do not...be afraid." (Dt 31:8)

Dt 31:1-8
Ps 32:3-4,7-9,12
Mt 18:1-5,10,12-14

Wednesday, August 12

WEEKDAY *(Green)*
ST. JANE FRANCES DE CHANTAL, WIFE, MOTHER, RELIGIOUS *(White)*

"If your brother sins against you, go to him and show him his fault. But do it privately, just between yourselves." (Mt 18:15)

Dt 34:1-12
Ps 66:1-3,5,8,16-17
Mt 18:15-20

Thursday, August 13

WEEKDAY *(Green)*
STS. PONTIAN, POPE AND MARTYR,
    AND HIPPOLYTUS, PRIEST AND MARTYR *(Red)*

"I forgave you the whole amount you owed me... because you asked me to. You should have had mercy on your fellow servant...as I had mercy on you." (Mt 18:32-33)

Jos 3:7-10a,11,13-17
Ps 114:1-6
Mt 18:21—19:1

Friday, August 14

ST. MAXIMILIAN KOLBE, PRIEST AND MARTYR *(Red)*

"[Jesus said], '...a man will...unite with his wife, and the two will become one... No human being must separate, then, what God has joined together.'" (Mt 19:5-6)

Jos 24:1-13
Ps 136:1-3,16-18,21-22,24
Mt 19:3-12

Saturday, August 15 *NOT a holy day this year.*

THE ASSUMPTION OF THE BLESSED VIRGIN MARY *(White)*

"A great and mysterious sight appeared in the sky... a woman, whose dress was the sun and who had the moon under her feet and a crown of twelve stars on her head." (Rv 12:1)

Rv 11:19a; 12:1-6a,10ab
Ps 45:10-12,16
1 Cor 15:20-27
Lk 1:39-56

LYNX KITTEN NEAR SANDSTONE, MINNESOTA

"With the gift of listening comes the gift of healing, because listening to your brother until he has said the last word in his heart is healing and consoling."

from *Poustinia: Encountering God in Silence, Solitude and Prayer*

Sunday, August 16

TWENTIETH SUNDAY IN ORDINARY TIME *(Green)*

"'My flesh is the real food; My blood is the real drink,' [Jesus said]. 'Those who eat My flesh and drink My blood live in Me, and I live in them.'" (Jn 6:55-56)

Prv 9:1-6
Ps 34:2-3,10-15
Eph 5:15-20
Jn 6:51-58

Monday, August 17

WEEKDAY *(Green)*

"Keep the commandments if you want to enter life." (Mt 19:17b)

Jgs 2:11-19
Ps 106:34-37,39-40,43,44
Mt 19:16-22

Tuesday, August 18

WEEKDAY *(Green)*

"[Jesus said], '...everyone who leaves [family] or fields for My sake will receive a hundred times more and will be given eternal life.'" (Mt 19:29)

Jgs 6:11-24a
Ps 85:9,11-14
Mt 19:23-30

Wednesday, August 19

WEEKDAY *(Green)*   ST. JOHN EUDES, PRIEST *(White)*

"Those who are last will be first, and those who are first will be last." (Mt 20:16)

Jgs 9:6-15
Ps 21:2-7
Mt 20:1-16

Thursday, August 20

ST. BERNARD, ABBOT AND DOCTOR *(White)*

"How I love to do Your will, my God! I keep Your teaching in my heart." (Ps 40:8)

Jgs 11:29-39a
Ps 40:5,7-10
Mt 22:1-14

Friday, August 21

ST. PIUS X, POPE *(White)*

"Love the Lord your God with all your heart...
soul and...mind... Love your neighbor as you love
yourself." (Mt 22:37,39)

Ru 1:1,3-6,14b-16,22
Ps 146:5-10
Mt 22:34-40

Saturday, August 22

THE QUEENSHIP OF THE BLESSED VIRGIN MARY *(White)*

"Happy are those who obey the LORD, who live
by His commands." (Ps 128:1)

Ru 2:1-3,8-11; 4:13-17
Ps 128:1-5
Mt 23:1-12

OZAUKEE COUNTY PARK IN WISCONSIN

"[Christ] is the Lord of History. He is the bridge between the Father and men... He offers Himself as *the* path. 'I am the way,' He said, 'to the Father.'"

from *Strannik: The Call to Pilgrimage for Western Man*

Sunday, August 23

TWENTY-FIRST SUNDAY IN ORDINARY TIME *(Green)*

"Husbands, love your wives just as Christ loved the church and gave His life for it." (Eph 5:25)

Jos 24:1-2a,15-17,18b
Ps 34:2-3,16-23
Eph 5:21-32
Jn 6:60-69

Monday, August 24

ST. BARTHOLOMEW, APOSTLE *(Red)*

"The LORD is faithful to His promises; He is merciful in all His acts." (Ps 145:13b)

Rv 21:9b-14
Ps 145:10-13,17-18
Jn 1:45-51

Tuesday, August 25

WEEKDAY *(Green)*   ST. LOUIS, HUSBAND, FATHER, KING *(White)*
ST. JOSEPH CALASANZ, PRIEST *(White)*

"We do not try to please people, but to please God, who tests our motives." (1 Thes 2:4c)

1 Thes 2:1-8
Ps 139:1-6
Mt 23:23-26

Wednesday, August 26

WEEKDAY *(Green)*

"God is at work in you who believe."
(1 Thes 2:13c)

1 Thes 2:9-13
Ps 139:7-12
Mt 23:27-32

Thursday, August 27

ST. MONICA, WIFE AND MOTHER *(White)*

"...you...must always be ready, because the Son of Man will come at an hour when you are not expecting Him." (Mt 24:44)

1 Thes 3:7-13
Ps 90:3-4,12-14,17
Mt 24:42-51

Friday, August 28

ST. AUGUSTINE, BISHOP AND DOCTOR *(White)*

"God did not call us to live in immorality, but in holiness. So then, whoever rejects this teaching is not rejecting a human being but God..." (1 Thes 4:7-8)

1 Thes 4:1-8
Ps 97:1-2,5-6,10-12
Mt 25:1-13

Saturday, August 29

THE PASSION OF ST. JOHN THE BAPTIST *(Red)*

"Make it your aim to live a quiet life, to mind your own business, and to earn your own living..." (1 Thes 4:11)

1 Thes 4:9-11
Ps 98:1,7-9
Mk 6:17-29

ROSEATA SPOONBILLS IN EVERGLADES NATIONAL PARK, FLORIDA

"Christ asks us to love our enemies. When we obey Christ's command to love as He loved us, we have the power, the grace and the charisms to change enemies into friends and beloved neighbors."

from *Light in the Darkness: A Christian Vision for Unstable Times*

Sunday, August 30

TWENTY-SECOND SUNDAY IN ORDINARY TIME *(Green)*

"What God the Father considers to be pure and genuine religion is this: to take care of orphans and widows in their suffering and to keep oneself from being corrupted by the world." (Jas 1:27)

Dt 4:1-2,6-8
Ps 15:2-5
Jas 1:17-18,21b-22,27
Mk 7:1-8,14-15,21-23

Monday, August 31

WEEKDAY *(Green)*

"...when the LORD comes...He will rule the peoples of the world with justice and fairness." (Ps 96:13)

1 Thes 4:13-18
Ps 96:1,3-5,11-13
Lk 4:16-30

Tuesday, September 1

WEEKDAY *(Green)*

"The LORD is my light and my salvation; I will fear no one." (Ps 27:1a)

1 Thes 5:1-6,9-11
Ps 27:1,4,13-14
Lk 4:31-37

Wednesday, September 2

WEEKDAY *(Green)*

"The gospel keeps bringing blessings and is spreading throughout the world..." (Col 1:6)

Col 1:1-8
Ps 52:10-11
Lk 4:38-44

Thursday, September 3

ST. GREGORY THE GREAT, POPE AND DOCTOR *(White)*

"We ask God to fill you with the knowledge of His will, with all the wisdom and understanding that His Spirit gives...[so] your lives will produce all kinds of good deeds..." (Col 1:9b,10b)

Col 1:9-14
Ps 98:2-6
Lk 5:1-11

Friday, September 4

WEEKDAY *(Green)*
CANADA: BLESSED DINA BELANGER, VIRGIN *(White)*

"Acknowledge that the LORD is God. He made us, and we belong to Him..." (Ps 100:3ab)

Col 1:15-20
Ps 100:1-5
Lk 5:33-39

Saturday, September 5

WEEKDAY *(Green)*   BLESSED VIRGIN MARY *(White)*

"I will gladly offer You a sacrifice, O LORD, I will give You thanks because You are good." (Ps 54:6)

Col 1:21-23
Ps 54:3-4,6,8
Lk 6:1-5

RED FOXES NEAR SANDSTONE, MINNESOTAS

"Our Lord said, 'Whatsoever you do to least of my brethren, you do to Me.' He was very explicit about it all. What we do for our brethren will be done to Him and earn us His gratitude."

from *The People of the Towel and the Water*

Sunday, September 6

TWENTY-THIRD SUNDAY IN ORDINARY TIME *(Green)*

"Tell everyone who is discouraged, 'Be strong and don't be afraid! God is coming to your rescue...'" (Is 35:4)

Is 35:4-7a
Ps 146:7-10
Jas 2:1-5
Mk 7:31-37

Monday, September 7 USA and CANADA: LABOR DAY

WEEKDAY *(Green)*

"...by means of my [St. Paul's] physical sufferings
I am helping to complete what still remains of
Christ's sufferings on behalf of His body, the
church." (Col 1:24b)

Weekday:
Col 1:24—2:3
Ps 62:6-7,9   or
Lk 6:6-11

Labor Day:
Gen 1:26—2:3 or Gen 2:4-9,15
Ps 90:2-4,12-14,16 or Ps 127:1-2
2 Thes 3:6-12,16
Mt 6:31-34 or Mt 25:14-30

Tuesday, September 8

THE NATIVITY OF THE BLESSED VIRGIN MARY *(White)*

"We know that in all things God works for good
with those who love Him..." (Rom 8:28a)

Mi 5:1-4a or Rom 8:28-30
Ps 13:5-6
Mt 1:1-16,18-23

Wednesday, September 9

ST. PETER CLAVER, PRIEST *(White)*

"Now you must get rid of...anger, passion and hateful feelings. No insults or obscene talk must ever come from your lips." (Col 3:8)

Col 3:1-11
Ps 145:2-3,10-13
Lk 6:20-26

Thursday, September 10

WEEKDAY *(Green)*

"Love your enemies and do good to them... You will then have a great reward, and you will be children of the Most High God." (Lk 6:35)

Col 3:12-17
Ps 150:1-6
Lk 6:27-38

ORDER FORM

To order copies of *Listen to the Spirit—He Will Lead You 2016 Prayer Journal*, please use the order blank printed below. Make checks or money orders payable to and mail to:

TRINITY PHOTOGRAPHY
3805 7th St. NE #109
Great Falls, MT 59404-1154

OR

PHONE orders: **1-888-220-5941** (toll free)
E-MAIL orders: **catholicprayerdiary@gmail.com**
ONLINE orders: **www.catholicprayerdiary.com**

COST IN U.S. DOLLARS

U.S.A.
1 - 4 journals . . . . **$16.99** each
5 - 9 journals . . . . **$15.99** each
10 or more journals . . .**$14.99** each

***** *WE PAY THE SHIPPING within the U.S.!!!* *****

CANADA Contact: **Madonna House Publications**,
2888 Dafoe Rd., Rt. 2, Combermere, Ontario K0J 1L0
1-888-703-7110 (toll free)
publications@madonnahouse.org
Madonna House has its own pricing and shipping policies.

I order _____ journal(s) at _____ each. *TOTAL: $_____*

Method of Payment: ___ **Check** ___ **Money Order** ___ **Discover**

___**Visa** ___**MasterCard** #_____

Expiration Date _____ **Signature** _____
(as your name appears on your card)

(Please PRINT)

Send to _____

Address _____

_____

City_____State_____

Zip Code_____Phone _____
(required for credit card purchases)

(Allow 2-3 weeks for delivery)

THANK YOU FOR YOUR ORDER!

TO ORDER PHOTOGRAPHS

If you would like to order prints of any of the photographs included in this calendar, or to inquire about obtaining permission to use any of them in your own publication, please contact Trinity Photography contact person, Sandy Wedel, to discuss size, finish, and other specifications, as well as to obtain prices.

Write: **Trinity Photography
ATTN: Sandy Wedel
3805 7th St. NE #109
Great Falls, MT 59404-1154**

E-Mail: **catholicprayerdiary@gmail.com**

Please include **your name** and **phone number** in any type of correspondence.

****

Visit our website at
http://www.catholicprayerdiary.com

Friday, September 11

WEEKDAY *(Green)*

"Why do you look at the speck in your brother's eye, but pay no attention to the log in your own eye?" (Lk 6:41)

1 Tm 1:1-2,12-14
Ps 16:1-2,5,7-8,11
Lk 6:39-42

Saturday, September 12

WEEKDAY *(Green)*   THE MOST HOLY NAME OF MARY *(White)*

"Christ Jesus came into the world to save sinners." (1 Tm 1:15)

1 Tm 1:15-17
Ps 113:1-7
Lk 6:43-49

MONUMENT VALLEY IN ARIZONA

"The greatest tragedy of our world is that men do not know, really know, that God loves them. Some believe it in a shadowy sort of way. If they were to really think about it, they would soon realize that their belief in God's love for them is very remote and abstract."

from *The Gospel Without Compromise*

Sunday, September 13

TWENTY-FOURTH SUNDAY IN ORDINARY TIME *(Green)*

"What good is there in your saying to [people in need], 'God bless you! Keep warm and eat well!' —if you don't give them the necessities of life? So it is with faith: if it is alone and includes no actions, then it is dead." (Jas 2:16-17)

Is 50:5-9a
Ps 116:1-6,8-9
Jas 2:14-18
Mk 8:27-35

Monday, September 14

THE EXALTATION OF THE HOLY CROSS *(Red)*

"...[Christ] humbled Himself and became
obedient unto death, even death on a cross."
(Phil 2:8)

Num 21:4b-9
Ps 78:1-2,34-38
Phil 2:6-11
Jn 3:13-17

Tuesday, September 15

OUR LADY OF SORROWS *(White)*

"Jesus saw His mother...standing [close to His
cross]." (Jn 19:26)

1 Tm 3:1-13
Ps 101:1-3,5-6
Jn 19:25-27 or Lk 2:33-35

Wednesday, September 16

ST. CORNELIUS, POPE AND MARTYR,
    AND ST. CYPRIAN, BISHOP AND MARTYR (Red)

"...the church of the living God [is] the pillar and support of the truth." (1 Tm 3:15)

1 Tm 3:14-16
Ps 111:1-6
Lk 7:31-35

Thursday, September 17

WEEKDAY (Green)
ST. ROBERT BELLARMINE, BISHOP AND DOCTOR (White)

"Watch yourself and watch your teaching... because if you do, you will save both yourself and those who hear you." (1 Tm 4:16)

1 Tm 4:12-16
Ps 111:7-10
Lk 7:36-50

Friday, September 18

WEEKDAY *(Green)*

"Whoever teaches a different doctrine and does
not agree with the true words of our Lord...is
swollen with pride and knows nothing."
(1 Tm 6:3-4)

1 Tm 6:2c-12
Ps 49:6-10,17-20
Lk 8:1-3

Saturday, September 19

WEEKDAY *(Green)*   ST. JANUARIUS, BISHOP AND MARTYR *(Red)*
BLESSED VIRGIN MARY *(White)*

"[Christ's] appearing will be brought about at the
right time by God...[who is] the King of kings and the
Lord of lords." (1 Tm 6:15)

1 Tm 6:13-16
Ps 100:2-5
Lk 8:4-15

A COUGAR NEAR SANDSTONE, MINNESOTA

"We make believe that we're [Christians]. We talk about the scriptures, but the scriptures are empty words unless you put them into practice. It's useless to listen and do nothing. It will be held against you if you know the scriptures and don't apply them."

from *Beginning Again: Recovering your innocence and joy through Confession*

Sunday, September 20

TWENTY-FIFTH SUNDAY IN ORDINARY TIME *(Green)*

"Where do all the fights and quarrels among you come from? They come from your desires for pleasure, which are constantly fighting within you." (Jas 4:1)

Wis 2:12,17-20
Ps 54:3-8
Jas 3:16—4:3
Mk 9:30-37

Monday, September 21

ST. MATTHEW, APOSTLE AND EVANGELIST *(Red)*

"Each one of us has received a special gift in proportion to what Christ has given." (Eph 4:7)

Eph 4:1-7,11-13
Ps 19:2-5
Mt 9:9-13

Tuesday, September 22

WEEKDAY *(Green)*

"Jesus said..., 'My mother and brothers are those who hear the word of God and obey it.'" (Lk 8:21)

Ezr 6:7-8,12b,14-20
Ps 122:1-5
Lk 8:19-21

Wednesday, September 23

ST. PIO OF PIETRELCINA, PRIEST *(White)*
CANADA: BLESSED EMILIE TAVERNIER-GAMELIN,
    WIFE, MOTHER, RELIGIOUS *(White)*

"Remember what God has done for you, and give thanks with all your heart." (Tob 13:6b)

Ezr 9:5-9
(Ps) Tob 13:2-4,6-8
Lk 9:1-6

Thursday, September 24

WEEKDAY *(Green)*

"The LORD takes pleasure in His people..." (Ps 149:4a)

Hag 1:1-8
Ps 149:1-6,9
Lk 9:7-9

Friday, September 25

WEEKDAY *(Green)*

"Send Your light and Your truth, [O God]; may they lead me..." (Ps 43:3a)

Hag 2:1-9
Ps 43:1-4
Lk 9:18-22

Saturday, September 26

WEEKDAY *(Green)*   STS. COSMAS AND DAMIAN, MARTYRS *(Red)*
CANADA: STS. JOHN DE BRÉBEUF AND ISAAC JOGUES,
    PRIESTS AND MARTYRS, AND COMPANIONS, MARTYRS *(Red)*

"[The LORD said to His people], 'Anyone who strikes you strikes what is most precious to Me.'" (Zech 2:8)

Zech 2:5-9,14-15a
(Ps) Jer 31:10-13
Lk 9:43b-45

ZION NATIONAL PARK, UTAH

"Our service must be service *in Christ*. We must act as Christ would act. We must ask ourselves each time, 'What would Christ do if He were I?'"

from *Sobornost: Eastern Unity of Mind and Heart for Western Man*

Sunday, September 27

TWENTY-SIXTH SUNDAY IN ORDINARY TIME *(Green)*

"[Jesus told them], 'If anyone should cause one of these little ones to lose faith in Me, it would be better for that person to have a large millstone tied around the neck and be thrown into the sea.'" (Mk 9:42)

Num 11:25-29
Ps 19:8,10,12-14
Jas 5:1-6
Mk 9:38-43,45,47-48

Monday, September 28

WEEKDAY *(Green)*   ST. WENCESLAUS, MARTYR *(Red)*
ST. LAWRENCE RUIZ AND COMPANIONS, MARTYRS *(Red)*

"...[Jesus] took a child...and said... 'Whoever welcomes this child in My name, welcomes Me...'" (Lk 9:47-48)

Zech 8:1-8
Ps 102:16-21,29,22-23
Lk 9:46-50

Tuesday, September 29

STS. MICHAEL, GABRIEL AND RAPHAEL, ARCHANGELS *(White)*

"Michael and his angels fought against the dragon...[which] was defeated, and [the dragon] and his angels were not allowed to stay in heaven any longer." (Rv 12:7,8)

Dan 7:9-10,13-14 or Rv 12:7-12a
Ps 138:1-5
Jn 1:47-51

Wednesday, September 30

ST. JEROME, PRIEST AND DOCTOR *(White)*

"You go and proclaim the Kingdom of God."
(Lk 9:60)

Neh 2:1-8
Ps 137:1-6
Lk 9:57-62

Thursday, October 1

ST. THÉRÈSE OF THE CHILD JESUS, VIRGIN AND DOCTOR *(White)*

"[Jesus said], 'Go! I am sending you like lambs among wolves.'" (Lk 10:3)

Neh 8:1-4a,5-6,7b-12
Ps 19:8-11
Lk 10:1-12

Friday, October 2

THE GUARDIAN ANGELS *(White)*

"The greatest in the Kingdom of heaven is the one who humbles himself and becomes like this little child." (Mt 18:4)

Bar 1:15-22
Ps 79:1-3,5,8-9
Mt 18:1-5,10

Saturday, October 3

WEEKDAY *(Green)*   BLESSED VIRGIN MARY *(White)*

"The LORD listens to those in need, and does not forget His people..." (Ps 69:33)

Bar 4:5-12,27-29
Ps 69:33-37
Lk 10:17-24

ROSS'S GEESE IN BOSQUE DEL APACHE, NEW MEXICO

"It seemed to me that [the rat race of frantic activity] could be the most subtle temptation yet presented by Satan to humanity. Such ceaseless activity would reduce men's understanding of the mystical, contemplative approach to God. It would also reduce prayer life to almost nothing."

from *Welcome, Pilgrim*

Sunday, October 4

TWENTY-SEVENTH SUNDAY IN ORDINARY TIME *(Green)*

"...a man will leave his father and mother and unite with his wife, and the two will become one." (Mk 10:7a)

Gen 2:18-24
Ps 128:1-6
Heb 2:9-11
Mk 10:2-16

Monday, October 5

WEEKDAY *(Green)*

"Love the Lord your God...and love your neighbor as you love yourself." (Lk 10:27)

Jon 1:1—2:2,11
(Ps) Jon 2:2-5,8
Lk 10:25-37

Tuesday, October 6

WEEKDAY *(Green)*   ST. BRUNO, PRIEST *(White)*
BLESSED MARIE-ROSE DUROCHER, VIRGIN *(White)*

"If You kept a record of our sins, [O LORD], who could escape being condemned? But You forgive us..." (Ps 130:3-4a)

Jon 3:1-10
Ps 130:1-4,7-8
Lk 10:38-42

Wednesday, October 7

OUR LADY OF THE ROSARY *(White)*

"I knew that You are a loving and merciful God, always patient...kind and...ready to change Your mind and not punish." (Jon 4:2)

Jon 4:1-11
Ps 86:3-6,9-10
Lk 11:1-4

Thursday, October 8

WEEKDAY *(Green)*

"'For you who obey Me,' [says the LORD Almighty], 'My saving power will rise on you like the sun and bring healing like the sun's rays.'" (Mal 3:20a)

Mal 3:13-20b
Ps 1:1-4,6
Lk 11:5-13

Friday, October 9

WEEKDAY *(Green)*
ST. DENIS, BISHOP AND MARTYR, AND COMPANIONS, MARTYRS *(Red)*
ST. JOHN LEONARDI, PRIEST *(White)*

"'Anyone who does not help Me gather is really scattering,' [Jesus told them]." (Lk 11:23b)

Jl 1:13-15; 2:1-2
Ps 9:2-3,6,8-9,16
Lk 11:15-26

Saturday, October 10

WEEKDAY *(Green)*   BLESSED VIRGIN MARY *(White)*

"Remember what the holy God has done and give thanks to Him." (Ps 97:12b)

Jl 4:12-21
Ps 97:1-2,5-6,11-12
Lk 11:27-28

GRAND TETON NATIONAL PARK, WYOMING

"...where love is, God is, and there His peace dwells."

from *Marriage: A Fountain of Grace*

Sunday, October 11

TWENTY-EIGHTH SUNDAY IN ORDINARY TIME *(Green)*

"[His disciples asked], 'Who...can be saved?' Jesus ...answered, 'This is impossible for human beings, but not for God; everything is possible for God.'" (Mk 10:26-27)

Wis 7:7-11
Ps 90:12-17
Heb 4:12-13
Mk 10:17-30

Monday, October 12

WEEKDAY *(Green)*

"May God our Father and the Lord Jesus Christ
give you grace and peace." (Rom 1:7b)

Rom 1:1-7
Ps 98:1-4
Lk 11:29-32

Tuesday, October 13

WEEKDAY *(Green)*

"[Those of evil ways] exchange the truth about
God for a lie; they worship and serve what God
has created instead of the Creator Himself, who
is to be praised forever!" (Rom 1:25)

Rom 1:16-25
Ps 19:2-5
Lk 11:37-41

Wednesday, October 14

WEEKDAY *(Green)*   ST. CALLISTUS I, POPE AND MARTYR *(Red)*

"Surely you know that God is kind, because He is trying to lead you to repent." (Rom 2:4b)

Rom 2:1-11
Ps 62:2-3,6-7,9
Lk 11:42-46

Thursday, October 15

ST. TERESA OF JESUS, VIRGIN AND DOCTOR *(White)*

"From the depths of my despair I call to You, LORD. Hear my cry." (Ps 130:1-2)

Rom 3:21-30
Ps 130:1-6
Lk 11:47-54

Friday, October 16

WEEKDAY *(Green)*   ST. HEDWIG, WIFE, MOTHER, RELIGIOUS *(White)*
ST. MARGARET MARY ALACOQUE, VIRGIN *(White)*
CANADA: ST. MARGUERITE D'YOUVILLE, RELIGIOUS *(White)*

"Be on guard against...hypocrisy. Whatever is covered up will be uncovered, and every secret will be made known." (Lk 12:1b-2)

Rom 4:1-8
Ps 32:1-2,5,11
Lk 12:1-7

Saturday, October 17

ST. IGNATIUS OF ANTIOCH, BISHOP AND MARTYR *(Red)*

"[The Lord] will keep His covenant forever." (Ps 105:8a)

Rom 4:13,16-18
Ps 105:6-9,42-43
Lk 12:8-12

SMOKY MOUNTAINS NATIONAL PARK, TENNESSEE

"'Stand firm as we do and don't be moved,' say the trees.'"

from *Welcome, Pilgrim*

Sunday, October 18

TWENTY-NINTH SUNDAY IN ORDINARY TIME *(Green)*

"Let us have confidence and approach God's throne where...we will receive mercy and find grace to help us just when we need it."
(Heb 4:16)

Is 53:10-11
Ps 33:4-5,18-20,22
Heb 4:14-16
Mk 10:35-45

Monday, October 19

STS. ISAAC JOGUES AND JOHN DE BRÉBEUF, PRIESTS
    AND MARTYRS, AND COMPANIONS, MARTYRS *(Red)*
CANADA: ST. PAUL OF THE CROSS, PRIEST *(White)*

"[Abraham] was absolutely sure that God would be able to do what He had promised. That is why he...'was accepted as righteous by God.'"
(Rom 4:21-22)

Rom 4:20-25
(Ps) Lk 1: 69-75
Lk 12:13-21

Tuesday, October 20

WEEKDAY *(Green)*   ST. PAUL OF THE CROSS, PRIEST *(White)*

"I am weak and poor, O LORD, but You have not forgotten me; ...hurry to my aid!" (Ps 40:17)

Rom 5:12,15b,17-19,20b-21
Ps 40:7-10,17
Lk 12:35-38

Wednesday, October 21

WEEKDAY *(Green)*

"...when you surrender yourselves...you are...the slaves of the master you obey—either of sin, [resulting] in death, or of obedience, [resulting] in being put right with God." (Rom 6:16)

Rom 6:12-18
Ps 124:1-8
Lk 12:39-48

Thursday, October 22

WEEKDAY *(Green)*   ST. JOHN PAUL II, POPE *(White)*
CANADA: DEDICATION OF CHURCHES *(White)*

"Sin pays its wage—death; but God's free gift is eternal life in union with Christ Jesus." (Rom 6:23)

Rom 6:19-23
Ps 1:1-4,6
Lk 12:49-53

Friday, October 23

WEEKDAY *(Green)*   ST. JOHN OF CAPISTRANO, PRIEST *(White)*

"Give me wisdom and knowledge, [O LORD],
because I trust in Your commands." (Ps 119:66)

Rom 7:18-25a
Ps 119:66,68,76-77,93-94
Lk 12:54-59

Saturday, October 24

WEEKDAY *(Green)*   ST. ANTHONY MARY CLARET, BISHOP *(White)*
BLESSED VIRGIN MARY *(White)*

"To be controlled by human nature results in
death; to be controlled by the Spirit results in
life and peace." (Rom 8:6)

Rom 8:1-11
Ps 24:1-6
Lk 13:1-9

NORTHERN ARIZONA

"This is the time of asking forgiveness of God and then of our neighbor. For we have all sinned against Him and against our neighbor. We still have time to repent, to cry out to God... 'Have mercy on me, O Lord, a sinner."

from *Urodivoi: Fools for God*

Sunday, October 25

THIRTIETH SUNDAY IN ORDINARY TIME *(Green)*

"The LORD says... 'I will guide [My people] to streams of water, on a smooth road where they will not stumble.'" (Jer 31:9bc)

Jer 31:7-9
Ps 126:1-6
Heb 5:1-6
Mk 10:46-52

Monday, October 26

WEEKDAY *(Green)*

"God's Spirit joins Himself to our spirits
to declare that we are God's children."
(Rom 8:16)

Rom 8:12-17
Ps 68:2,4,6-7,20-21
Lk 13:10-17

Tuesday, October 27

WEEKDAY *(Green)*

"I consider that what we suffer at this present
time cannot be compared at all with the glory
that is going to be revealed to us." (Rom 8:18)

Rom 8:18-25
Ps 126:1-6
Lk 13:18-21

Wednesday, October 28

STS. SIMON AND JUDE, APOSTLES *(Red)*

"...you are...citizens together with God's people and members of the family of God." (Eph 2:19b)

Eph 2:19-22
Ps 19:2-5
Lk 6:12-19

Thursday, October 29

WEEKDAY *(Green)*

"If God is for us, who can be against us?" (Rom 8:31b)

Rom 8:31b-39
Ps 109:21-22,26-27,30-31
Lk 13:31-35

Friday, October 30

WEEKDAY *(Green)*

"May God, who rules over all, be praised forever! Amen." (Rom 9:5c)

Rom 9:1-5
Ps 147:12-15,19-20
Lk 14:1-6

Saturday, October 31 HALLOWEEN

WEEKDAY *(Green)*   BLESSED VIRGIN MARY *(White)*

"Those who make themselves great will be humbled, and those who humble themselves will be made great." (Lk 14:11)

Rom 11:1-2a,11-12,25-29
Ps 94:12-15,17-18
Lk 14:1,7-11

SAGUARO CACTI IN SAGUARO NATIONAL PARK, ARIZONA

"Courage is not the absence of fear, but fear overcome by faith. How can we doubt that our life is glorious when it is God who has called us to this life?"

from *Living the Gospel Without Compromise*

Sunday, November 1

HOLY DAY OF OBLIGATION   *Daylight Savings Time Ends*

ALL SAINTS *(White)*

"Happy are the pure in heart; they will see God!"
(Mt 5:8)

Rv 7:2-4,9-14
Ps 24:1-6
1 Jn 3:1-3
Mt 5:1-12a

Monday, November 2 ALL SOULS DAY

THE COMMEMORATION OF ALL THE FAITHFUL DEPARTED *(White/Violet/Black)*

"[Jesus said], 'I will never turn away anyone who comes to Me.'" (Jn 6:37b)

Wis 3:1-9
Ps 27:1,4,7-9,13-14
Rom 5:5-11 or Rom 6:3-9
Jn 6:37-40

Tuesday, November 3

WEEKDAY *(Green)*   ST. MARTIN DE PORRES, RELIGIOUS *(White)*

"How happy are those who will sit down at the feast in the Kingdom of God!" (Lk 14:15b)

Rom 12:5-16b
Ps 131:1-3
Lk 14:15-24

Wednesday, November 4

ST. CHARLES BORROMEO, BISHOP *(White)*

"...the only obligation you have is to love one another. Whoever does this has obeyed the Law." (Rom 13:8)

Rom 13:8-10
Ps 112:1-2,4-5,9
Lk 14:25-33

Thursday, November 5

WEEKDAY *(Green)*

"'As surely as I am the living God,' says the Lord, 'everyone will kneel before Me, and everyone will confess that I am God.'" (Rom 14:11)

Rom 14:7-12
Ps 27:1,4,13-14
Lk 15:1-10

ORDER FORM

To order copies of *Listen to the Spirit—He Will Lead You 2016 Prayer Journal,* please use the order blank printed below. Make checks or money orders payable to and mail to:

TRINITY PHOTOGRAPHY
3805 7th St. NE #109
Great Falls, MT 59404-1154

OR

PHONE orders: **1-888-220-5941** (toll free)
E-MAIL orders: **catholicprayerdiary@gmail.com**
ONLINE orders: **www.catholicprayerdiary.com**

COST IN U.S. DOLLARS

U.S.A.   **1 - 4** journals . . . . **$16.99** each
              5 - 9 journals . . . . **$15.99** each
              10 or more journals . . .**$14.99** each

***** *WE PAY THE SHIPPING within the U.S.!!!* *****

CANADA   Contact: **Madonna House Publications,**
2888 Dafoe Rd., Rt. 2, Combermere, Ontario K0J 1L0
1-888-703-7110 (toll free)
publications@madonnahouse.org
Madonna House has its own pricing and shipping policies.

I order _____ journal(s) at _____ each. *TOTAL: $_____*

Method of Payment: ___ **Check**   ___ **Money Order**   ___ **Discover**

___**Visa**   ___**MasterCard #**_____

Expiration Date _____ **Signature** _____
                                          (as your name appears on your card)

(Please PRINT)

Send to _____

Address _____

_____

City_____State_____

Zip Code_____Phone _____
                                          (required for credit card purchases)

(Allow 2-3 weeks for delivery)

THANK YOU FOR YOUR ORDER!

TO ORDER PHOTOGRAPHS

If you would like to order prints of any of the photographs included in this calendar, or to inquire about obtaining permission to use any of them in your own publication, please contact Trinity Photography contact person, Sandy Wedel, to discuss size, finish, and other specifications, as well as to obtain prices.

Write: **Trinity Photography**
ATTN: Sandy Wedel
3805 7th St. NE #109
Great Falls, MT 59404-1154

Phone: **1-888-220-5941**

E-Mail: **catholicprayerdiary@gmail.com**

Please include **your name** and **phone number** in any type of correspondence.

****

Visit our website at
http://www.catholicprayerdiary.com

Friday, November 6

WEEKDAY *(Green)*

"Sing a new song to the LORD; He has done wonderful things!" (Ps 98:1a)

Rom 15:14-21
Ps 98:1-4
Lk 16:1-8

Saturday, November 7

WEEKDAY *(Green)*   BLESSED VIRGIN MARY *(White)*

"You cannot serve both God and money." (Lk 16:13c)

Rom 16:3-9,16,22-27
Ps 145:2-5,10-11
Lk 16:9-15

SUNSET IN NORTHERN MANITOBA, CANADA

"Faith is a pulsating thing; a light, a sun that nothing can dim if it exists in the hearts of men. That's why it's so beautiful. God gives it to me saying, 'I love you. Do you love Me back? Come and follow Me in the darkness. I want to know if you are ready to go into the things that you do not see yet, on faith alone."

from *Re-Entry into Faith: "Courage—be not afraid!"*

Sunday, November 8

THIRTY-SECOND SUNDAY IN ORDINARY TIME

"'I tell you that this poor widow put more in the offering box than all the others,' [Jesus said]. 'For the others put in what they had to spare of their riches; but she...put in all she had...'" (Mk 12:43-44)

1 Kgs 17:10-16
Ps 146:7-10
Heb 9:24-28
Mk 12:38-44

Monday, November 9

THE DEDICATION OF THE LATERAN BASILICA IN ROME *(White)*

"God's temple is holy, and you yourselves are His temple." (1 Cor 3:17b)

Ez 47:1-2,8-9,12
Ps 84:3-6,8,11
1 Cor 3:9c-11,16-17
Jn 2:13-22

Tuesday, November 10

ST. LEO THE GREAT, POPE AND DOCTOR *(White)*

"Those who have put their trust in God will come to understand the truth of His ways." (Wis 3:9)

Wis 2:23—3:9
Ps 34:2-3,16-19
Lk 17:7-10

Wednesday, November 11

ST. MARTIN OF TOURS, BISHOP *(White)*

"[The Lord] Himself made everyone, great and
common alike, and He provides for all equally, but
He will judge the conduct of rulers more strictly."
(Wis 6:7-8)

Wis 6:1-11
Ps 82:3-4,6-7
Lk 17:11-19

Thursday, November 12

ST. JOSAPHAT, BISHOP AND MARTYR *(Red)*

"[Wisdom] loves what is good. It is sharp and
unconquerable, kind, and a friend of humanity."
(Wis 7:22f-23a)

Wis 7:22b—8:1
Ps 119:89-91,130,135,175
Lk 17:20-25

Friday, November 13

ST. FRANCES XAVIER CABRINI, VIRGIN *(White)* (USA)

"Anyone who does not know God is simply foolish. [They] look at the good things around them and still fail to see the living God." (Wis 13:1ab)

Wis 13:1-9
Ps 19:2-5
Lk 17:26-37

Saturday, November 14

WEEKDAY *(Green)*   BLESSED VIRGIN MARY *(White)*

"Jesus [taught His disciples] that they should always pray and never become discouraged." (Lk 18:1)

Wis 18:14-16; 19:6-9
Ps 105:2-3,36-37,42-43
Lk 18:1-8

CHOLLA CACTI IN JOSHUA TREE NATIONAL PARK, CALIFORNIA

"Let us work on our faults, on our sins of omission and commission. Let us be watchful over them so as to eliminate them. Be ready to have prickings of conscience constantly; these prickings will function to develop in you a very delicate conscience."

from *Beginning Again: Recovering your innocence and joy through Confession*

Sunday, November 15

THIRTY-THIRD SUNDAY IN ORDINARY TIME *(Green)*

"'Heaven and earth will pass away,' [Jesus said],
'but My words will never pass away.'" (Mk 13:31)

Dan 12:1-3
Ps 16:5,8-11
Heb 10:11-14,18
Mk 13:24-32

Monday, November 16

WEEKDAY *(Green)*
ST. MARGARET OF SCOTLAND, WIFE AND QUEEN *(White)*
ST. GERTRUDE THE GREAT, VIRGIN *(White)*

"When I see the wicked breaking Your law,
[O Lord], I am filled with anger." (Ps 119:53)

1 Mac 1:10-15,41-43,54-57,62-63
Ps 119:53,61,134,150,155,158
Lk 18:35-43

Tuesday, November 17

ST. ELIZABETH OF HUNGARY, WIFE, MOTHER, RELIGIOUS *(White)*

"I lie down and sleep, and all night long the
Lord protects me." (Ps 3:5)

2 Mac 6:18-31
Ps 3:2-8
Lk 19:1-10

Wednesday, November 18

WEEKDAY *(Green)*   THE DEDICATION OF THE BASILICAS OF
   STS. PETER AND PAUL, APOSTLES *(White)*
ST. ROSE PHILIPPINE DUCHESNE, VIRGIN *(White)* (USA)

"[The woman said to her son], 'I was not the one
who gave you life and breath and put together each
part of your body. It was God who did it...'"
(2 Mac 7:22b-23a)

2 Mac 7:1,20-31
Ps 17:1,5-6,8,15
Lk 19:11-28

Thursday, November 19

WEEKDAY *(Green)*

"Let the giving of thanks be your sacrifice to
God..." (Ps 50:14)

1 Mac 2:15-29
Ps 50:1-2,5-6,14-15
Lk 19:41-44

Friday, November 20

WEEKDAY *(Green)*

"[LORD God]...everything in heaven and earth is
Yours, and You are king, supreme ruler over all."
(1 Chr 29:11b)

1 Mac 4:36-37,52-59
(Ps): 1 Chr 29:10-12
Lk 19:45-48

Saturday, November 21

THE PRESENTATION OF THE BLESSED VIRGIN MARY *(White)*

"I will sing with joy because of You. I will sing
praise to You, Almighty God." (Ps 9:2)

1 Mac 6:1-13
Ps 9:2-4,6,16,19
Lk 20:27-40

GLACIER NATIONAL PARK, MONTANA

"Out of the wind that always seems to surround me, I hear a voice: 'Be at peace. I am with you unto the end of time. What is happening I cannot control because I have given people freedom, and people are exercising their freedom. But I am with you unto the end of time."

from *Urodivoi: Fools for God*

Sunday, November 22

OUR LORD JESUS CHRIST, KING OF THE UNIVERSE *(White)*

"Jesus Christ...the ruler of the kings of the world...
loves us, ...has freed us from our sins and made us
a kingdom of priests to serve His God and Father.
To Jesus be the glory and power forever and ever!"
(Rv 1:5-6)

Dan 7:13-14
Ps 93:1-2,5
Rv 1:5-8
Jn 18:33b-37

Monday, November 23

WEEKDAY *(Green)*   ST. CLEMENT I, POPE AND MARTYR *(Red)*
ST. COLUMBAN, ABBOT *(White)*
BLESSED MIGUEL AGUSTÍN PRO, PRIEST AND MARTYR *(Red)*

"[O LORD], may You be praised as You sit on Your royal throne. May hymns be sung to Your glory forever." (Dan 3:54)

Dan 1:1-6,8-20
(Ps) Dan 3:52-56
Lk 21:1-4

Tuesday, November 24

ST. ANDREW DUNG-LAC, PRIEST AND MARTYR,
    AND COMPANIONS, MARTYRS *(Red)*

"Jesus said, '...don't be fooled. Many...claiming to speak for Me will come and say, ...*The time has come!* But don't follow them.'" (Lk 21:8)

Dan 2:31-45
(Ps) Dan 3:57-61
Lk 21:5-11

Wednesday, November 25

WEEKDAY *(Green)*
ST. CATHERINE OF ALEXANDRIA, VIRGIN AND MARTYR *(Red)*

"'Stand firm and you will save yourselves,'
[Jesus said]." (Lk 21:19)

Dan 5:1-6,13-14,16-17,23-28
(Ps) Dan 3:62-67
Lk 21:12-19

Thursday, November 26   USA: THANKSGIVING DAY

WEEKDAY *(Green)*   *Thanksgiving Ritual Mass (White)*

"Give praise to the God of the universe, who...deals
with us mercifully. May He give us happiness and
allow us to have peace...forever." (Sir 50:22-23)

Weekday Mass:

Dan 6:12-28
(Ps) Dan 3:68-74
Lk 21:20-28

Thanksgiving Day Mass:

Sir 50:22-24
Ps 67:2-3,5,7-8
1 Cor 1:3-9
Lk 17:11-19

Friday, November 27

WEEKDAY *(Green)*

"...sing [the Lord's] praise and honor Him forever."
(Dan 3:75b)

Dan 7:2-14
(Ps) Dan 3:75-81
Lk 21:29-33

Saturday, November 28

WEEKDAY *(Green)*   BLESSED VIRGIN MARY *(White)*

"Praise the LORD, all faithful people; sing His
praise and honor Him forever." (Dan 3:86)

Dan 7:15-27
(Ps) Dan 3:82-87
Lk 21:34-36

A GREAT BLUE HERON IN BOSQUE DEL APACHE, NEW MEXICO

"Advent is the season for waiting, waiting for the Savior to appear."

from *Dear Parents: A Gift of Love for Families*

Sunday, November 29

FIRST SUNDAY OF ADVENT *(Violet)*

"May the Lord make your love for one another and for all people grow... In this way...you will be perfect and holy in the presence of our God and Father when our Lord Jesus comes with all who belong to Him." (1 Thes 3:12-13)

Jer 33:14-16
Ps 25:4-5,8-10,14
1 Thes 3:12—4:2
Lk 21:25-28,34-36

Monday, November 30

ST. ANDREW, APOSTLE *(Red)*

"Faith comes from hearing the message, and the
message comes through preaching Christ."
(Rom 10:17)

Rom 10:9-18
Ps 19:2-5
Mt 4:18-22

Tuesday, December 1

ADVENT WEEKDAY *(Violet)*

"...a new king will arise... The land will be as full
of knowledge of the LORD as the seas are full of
water." (Is 11:1,9b)

Is 11:1-10
Ps 72:1,7-8,12-13,17
Lk 10:21-24

Wednesday, December 2

ADVENT WEEKDAY *(Violet)*

"He is the LORD! We have put our trust in Him, and now we are happy and joyful because He has saved us." (Is 25:9b)

Is 25:6-10a
Ps 23:1-6
Mt 15:29-37

Thursday, December 3

ST. FRANCIS XAVIER, PRIEST *(White)*

"[Jesus said], 'Anyone who hears [My words] and obeys them is like a wise man who built his house on rock.'" (Mt 7:24)

Is 26:1-6
Ps 118:1,8-9,19-21,25-27
Mt 7:21,24-27

Friday, December 4

ADVENT WEEKDAY *(Violet)*
ST. JOHN OF DAMASCUS, PRIEST AND DOCTOR *(White)*

"When [the day of the LORD] comes...it will be the end of those who oppress others and show contempt for God." (Is 29:18,20)

Is 29:17-24
Ps 27:1-4,13-14
Mt 9:27-31

Saturday, December 5

ADVENT WEEKDAY *(Violet)*

"The LORD will make you go through hard times, but He Himself will be there to teach you, and you will not have to search for Him any more." (Is 30:20b)

Is 30:19-21,23-26
Ps 147:1-6
Mt 9:35—10:1,5a,6-8

THE AURORA BOREALIS OVER NORTHERN MANITOBA, CANADA

"[Christ] comes to us now, establishing a New Covenant in our hearts, with the task of delivering us from the power of Satan and bringing us into His kingdom."

from *Donkey Bells: Advent and Christmas*

Sunday, December 6

SECOND SUNDAY OF ADVENT *(Violet)*

"I am sure that God, who began this good work in you, will carry it on until it is finished on the Day of Christ Jesus." (Phil 1:6)

Bar 5:1-9
Ps 126:1-6
Phil 1:4-6,8-11
Lk 3:1-6

Monday, December 7

ST. AMBROSE, BISHOP AND DOCTOR *(White)*

"Those whom the LORD has rescued will travel home by ['The Road of Holiness']." (Is 35:9b)

Is 35:1-10
Ps 85:9-14
Lk 5:17-26

Tuesday, December 8 *HOLY DAY OF OBLIGATION*

IMMACULATE CONCEPTION OF THE BLESSED VIRGIN MARY *(White)*
Patronal Feastday of the United States of America

"All things are done according to God's plan and decision." (Eph 1:11a)

Gen 3:9-15,20
Ps 98:1-4
Eph 1:3-6,11-12
Lk 1:26-38

Wednesday, December 9

ADVENT WEEKDAY *(Violet)*
ST. JUAN DIEGO CUAUHTLATOATZIN, HERMIT *(White)*

"The LORD is the everlasting God; He created all the world. He never grows tired or weary."
(Is 40:28)

Is 40:25-31
Ps 103:1-4,8,10
Mt 11:28-30

Thursday, December 10

ADVENT WEEKDAY *(Violet)*

"I am the LORD your God; I strengthen you and tell you, 'Do not be afraid; I will help you.'"
(Is 41:13)

Is 41:13-20
Ps 145:1,9-13
Mt 11:11-15

Friday, December 11

ADVENT WEEKDAY (*Violet*) ST. DAMASUS I, POPE (*White*)

"God's wisdom...is shown to be true by its results." (Mt 11:19c)

Is 48:17-19
Ps 1:1-4,6
Mt 11:16-19

Saturday, December 12

OUR LADY OF GUADALUPE (*White*)
  Patroness of the Americas

"Now God's salvation has come! Now God has shown His power as King!" (Rv 12:10ab)

Zech 2:14-17 or Rv 11:19a; 12:1-6a,10ab
(Ps) Lk 1:46-55
Lk 1:26-38 or Lk 1:39-47

SUNRISE IN NORTHERN MANITOBA, CANADA

"The birthday of Christ! ...Christmas is the first love letter of God to man, a love letter called the Incarnation."

from *Dear Parents: A Gift of Love for Families*

Sunday, December 13

THIRD SUNDAY OF ADVENT *(Violet)*

"The LORD will take delight in you, and in His love He will give you new life." (Zeph 3:17b)

Zeph 3:14-18a
Ps 12:2-6
Phil 4:4-7
Lk 3:10-18

Monday, December 14

ST. JOHN OF THE CROSS, PRIEST AND DOCTOR *(White)*

"Teach me to live according to Your truth, for You are my God, who saves me." (Ps 25:5ab)

Num 24:2-7,15-17a
Ps 25:4-9
Mt 21:23-27

Tuesday, December 15

ADVENT WEEKDAY *(Violet)*

"The righteous call to the LORD and He listens; He rescues them from all their troubles." (Ps 34:17)

Zeph 3:1-2,9-13
Ps 34:2-3,6-7,17-19,23
Mt 21:28-32

Wednesday, December 16

ADVENT WEEKDAY *(Violet)*

"Human loyalty will reach up from the earth, and God's righteousness will look down from heaven." (Ps 85:11)

Is 45:6b-8,18,21b-25
Ps 85:9-10,11-12,13-14
Lk 7:18b-23

Thursday, December 17

ADVENT WEEKDAY *(Violet)*

"May all nations ask God to bless them..." (Ps 72:17c)

Gen 49:2,8-10
Ps 72:3-4,7-8,17
Mt 1:1-17

Friday, December 18

ADVENT WEEKDAY *(Violet)*

"[Mary] found out that she was going to have a baby by the Holy Spirit." (Mt 1:18d)

Jer 23:5-8
Ps 72:1,12-13,18-19
Mt 1:18-25

Saturday, December 19

ADVENT WEEKDAY *(Violet)*

"Sovereign LORD, I put my hope in You."
(Ps 71:5a)

Jgs 13:2-7,24-25a
Ps 71:3-6,16-17
Lk 1:5-25

THE SKY OVER ZION NATIONAL PARK, UTAH

"[C]hrist is the Light of the world, come to light our darkened world."

from *Donkey Bells: Advent and Christmas*

Sunday, December 20

FOURTH SUNDAY OF ADVENT *(Violet)*

"Elizabeth was filled with the Holy Spirit and said in a loud voice, 'You [Mary] are the most blessed of all women, and blessed is the child you will bear!'" (Lk 1:41b-42)

Mi 5:1-4a
Ps 80:2-3,15-16,18-19
Heb 10:5-10
Lk 1:39-45

Monday, December 21

ADVENT WEEKDAY *(Violet)*
ST. PETER CANISIUS, PRIEST AND DOCTOR *(White)*

"This is the time for singing; the song of doves is heard in the fields." (Sg 2:12)

Sg 2:8-14 or Zeph 3:14-18a
Ps 33:2-3,11-12,20-21
Lk 1:39-45

Tuesday, December 22

ADVENT WEEKDAY *(Violet)*

"The LORD has filled my heart with joy; how happy I am because of what He has done!" (1 Sam 2:1a)

1 Sam 1:24-28
(Ps) 1 Sam 2:1,4-8
Lk 1:46-56

Wednesday, December 23

ADVENT WEEKDAY *(Violet)*   ST. JOHN OF KANTY, PRIEST *(White)*

"The LORD is the friend of those who obey Him and He affirms His covenant with them."
(Ps 25:14)

Mal 3:1-4,23-24
Ps 25:4-5,8-10,14
Lk 1:57-66

Thursday, December 24   CHRISTMAS EVE

ADVENT WEEKDAY *(Violet)*

"Our God...will cause the bright dawn of salvation to rise on us...to guide our steps into the path of peace." (Lk 1:78,79b)

2 Sam 7:1-5,8b-12,14a,16
Ps 89:2-5,27,29
Lk 1:67-79
Vigil of Christmas Readings: see Appendix

Friday, December 25 CHRISTMAS - HOLY DAY OF OBLIGATION

THE NATIVITY OF THE LORD *(White)*

"This very day in David's town your Savior was
born—Christ the Lord." (Lk 2:11)

Readings: see Appendix

Saturday, December 26 CANADA: BOXING DAY

ST. STEPHEN, THE FIRST MARTYR *(Red)*

"They kept on stoning Stephen as he called out
to the Lord, 'Lord Jesus, receive my spirit!'"
(Acts 7:59)

Acts 6:8-10; 7:54-59
Ps 31:3-4,6-8,17,21
Mt 10:17-22

POLAR BEARS IN NORTHERN MANITOBA, CANADA

"Children look at their parents and hope that their parents are sure of something, someone, that they have no doubts about the fundamentals of life, especially God."

from *In the Furnace of Doubts: Meditations—when you've lost your answers*

Sunday, December 27

THE HOLY FAMILY OF JESUS, MARY AND JOSEPH *(White)*

"Everything you do or say...should be done in the name of the Lord Jesus, as you give thanks through Him to God the Father." (Col 3:17)

Sir 3:2-6,12-14 or 1 Sam 1:20-22,24-28
Ps 128:1-5
Col 3:12-21 or 1 Jn 3:1-2,21-24
Lk 2:41-52

Monday, December 28

THE HOLY INNOCENTS, MARTYRS *(Red)*

"If we say that we have fellowship with [God], yet at the same time live in the darkness, we are lying both in our words and in our actions." (1 Jn 1:6)

1 Jn 1:5—2:2
Ps 124:2-5,7-8
Mt 2:13-18

Tuesday, December 29

FIFTH DAY WITHIN THE OCTAVE OF CHRISTMAS *(White)*
ST. THOMAS BECKET, BISHOP AND MARTYR *(White for Christmas)*

"If we love others, we live in the light, and so there is nothing in us that will cause someone else to sin." (1 Jn 2:10)

1 Jn 2:3-11
Ps 96:1-3,5-6
Lk 2:22-35

Wednesday, December 30

SIXTH DAY WITHIN THE OCTAVE OF CHRISTMAS *(White)*

"The world and everything in it that people desire is passing away; but those who do the will of God live forever." (1 Jn 2:17)

1 Jn 2:12-17
Ps 96:7-10
Lk 2:36-40

Thursday, December 31 NEW YEAR'S EVE

SEVENTH DAY WITHIN THE OCTAVE OF CHRISTMAS *(White)*
ST. SYLVESTER I, POPE *(White)*

"Out of the fullness of [the Word's] grace He has blessed us all, giving us one blessing after another." (Jn 1:16)

1 Jn 2:18-21
Ps 96:1-2,11-13
Jn 1:1-18

APPENDIX

DAY OF PRAYER FOR THE LEGAL PROTECTION OF THE UNBORN (January 22)

Gen 1:1—2:2 or 2 Mac 7:1,20-31 or Is 49:1-6 or Rom 11:33-36 or
    Eph 1:3-14 or Eph 3:14-21 or Col 1:12-20 or 1 Jn 3:11-21
Mt 18:1-5,10,12-14 or Mk 9:30-37 or Lk 1:39-56 or Lk 17:11-19
    or Lk 23:35-43 or Jn 1:1-5,9-14,16-18 or Jn 6:24-35

EASTER VIGIL (April 4)

Gen 1:1—2:2 (Ps 104:1-2,5-6,10,12,13-14,24,35)
Gen 22:1-18 (Ps 16:5,8-11)
Ex 14:15—15:1 (Ps - Ex:15:1-6,17-18)
Is 54:5-14 (Ps 30:2,4-6,11-13)
Is 55:1-11 (Ps - Is 12:2-6)
Bar 3:9-15,32—4:4 (Ps 19:8-11)
Ez 36:16-17a,18-28 (Ps 42:3,5; 43:3,4)
Rom 6:3-11 (Ps 118:1-2,16-17,22-23)
Mk 16:1-7

CHRISTMAS (December 24 and 25)

<u>Vigil Mass</u>
Is 62:1-5
Ps 89:4-5,16-17,27,29
Acts 13:16-17,22-25
Mt 1:1-25

<u>Night or Midnight Mass</u>
Is 9:1-6
Ps 96:1-3,11-13
Ti 2:11-14
Lk 2:1-14

<u>Mass at Dawn</u>
Is 62:11-12
Ps 97:1,6,11-12
Ti 3:4-7
Lk 2:15-20

<u>Mass during the Day</u>
Is 52:7-10
Ps 98:1-6
Heb 1:1-6
Jn 1:1-18

2016

JANUARY
S	M	T	W	T	F	S
					1	2
3	4	5	6	7	8	9
10	11	12	13	14	15	16
17	18	19	20	21	22	23
24	25	26	27	28	29	30
31						

JULY
S	M	T	W	T	F	S
					1	2
3	4	5	6	7	8	9
10	11	12	13	14	15	16
17	18	19	20	21	22	23
24	25	26	27	28	29	30
31						

FEBRUARY
S	M	T	W	T	F	S
	1	2	3	4	5	6
7	8	9	10	11	12	13
14	15	16	17	18	19	20
21	22	23	24	25	26	27
28	29					

AUGUST
S	M	T	W	T	F	S
	1	2	3	4	5	6
7	8	9	10	11	12	13
14	15	16	17	18	19	20
21	22	23	24	25	26	27
28	29	30	31			

MARCH
S	M	T	W	T	F	S
		1	2	3	4	5
6	7	8	9	10	11	12
13	14	15	16	17	18	19
20	21	22	23	24	25	26
27	28	29	30	31		

SEPTEMBER
S	M	T	W	T	F	S
				1	2	3
4	5	6	7	8	9	10
11	12	13	14	15	16	17
18	19	20	21	22	23	24
25	26	27	28	29	30	

APRIL
S	M	T	W	T	F	S
					1	2
3	4	5	6	7	8	9
10	11	12	13	14	15	16
17	18	19	20	21	22	23
24	25	26	27	28	29	30

OCTOBER
S	M	T	W	T	F	S
						1
2	3	4	5	6	7	8
9	10	11	12	13	14	15
16	17	18	19	20	21	22
23	24	25	26	27	28	29
30	31					

MAY
S	M	T	W	T	F	S
1	2	3	4	5	6	7
8	9	10	11	12	13	14
15	16	17	18	19	20	21
22	23	24	25	26	27	28
29	30	31				

NOVEMBER
S	M	T	W	T	F	S
		1	2	3	4	5
6	7	8	9	10	11	12
13	14	15	16	17	18	19
20	21	22	23	24	25	26
27	28	29	30			

JUNE
S	M	T	W	T	F	S
			1	2	3	4
5	6	7	8	9	10	11
12	13	14	15	16	17	18
19	20	21	22	23	24	25
26	27	28	29	30		

DECEMBER
S	M	T	W	T	F	S
				1	2	3
4	5	6	7	8	9	10
11	12	13	14	15	16	17
18	19	20	21	22	23	24
25	26	27	28	29	30	31